CW00819057

Microscopy
on a
Shoestring
for
Beekeepers and Naturalists

NORTHERN BEE BOOKS ● HEBDEN BRIDGE
WEST YORKSHIRE, U.K.

BEEKEEPING EDUCATION SERVICE ● CHESHIRE
CONNECTICUT, U.S.A.

MICROSCOPY on a SHOESTRING
for
BEEKEEPERS and NATURALISTS

A guide for beekeepers and naturalists for the salient points of dissecting and compound microscopes, for dissection and for the production of permanent microscope slides.

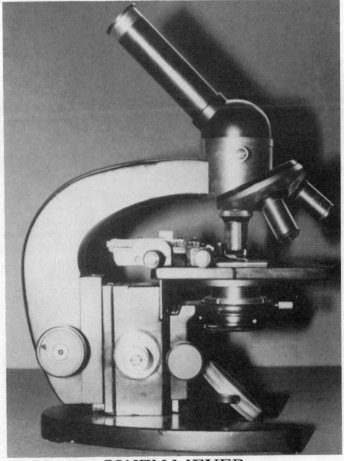

OWEN MEYER

British Library C.I.P.

Meyer, Owen
Microscopy on a shoestring for beekeepers and
naturalists
1. Microscope and microscopy   2. Bees
I. Title
578   QH205.2

ISBN 0-907908-10-1

Library of Congress Catalog Card No. 84-18492

Library of Congress C.I.P.

Bibliography: p.
Includes index.
1. Microscope and microscopy. 2. Dissection.
3. Mounting of microscope specimens. 4. Honey bee—
Diseases—Diagnosis. 5. Honey bee. 6. Bee culture.
I. Title.
QH205.2.M49   1984   578'.9   84-18492

ISBN 0 907908-10-1

Printed by G. Beard & Son Limited, Brighton

CONTENTS

INTRODUCTION

This book grew out of talks I have given up and down the country on simple microscopy. In these talks it was not possible, nor desirable, to give precise details of the various processes discussed and friends were kind enough to encourage me to get down on paper some of the simple techniques used in the production of microscope slides.

I had better say for what kind of reader the book is meant. It is intended as a reference book for the work bench of the keen amateur who has a microscope or is intending to get one and wants to get the best out of his instrument, to find out more about how his bees are made, how they function, what the pathogens are like which, alas, sometimes attack our bees and how simple microscopic techniques can re-inforce and confirm the clinical diagnosis of disease. I hope too that the amateur naturalist will find what I have said of use in his particular field. Although I refer throughout specifically to bees, practically all the techniques can be used with other insects.

If I seem to have emphasised the DIY aspect it is because many of my readers will be interested in the subject on a hobby basis and will not want to spend vast sums of money on apparatus they will want to use only occasionally. For instance, there is a very good hotplate on the market for about £90. My hotplate cost literally a few pence – most of it was made from scrap. As I have said elsewhere, in order to make these things the underlying principles have to be understood. This is an advantage. So too is the fact that the home made article is capable of modification to meet particular needs.

Bees are singularly well suited for microscopic examination. Their bodies are small so that the internal organs are even smaller (but not so small as might be supposed). Dissection is simple and clean. There are no all pervading masses of blood vessels or sheets of adipose tissue to be cleared away before anything can be seen. The external skeleton too simplifies investigation.

Under "Methods for Specific Material" I have dealt with only a small selection of parts which make interesting and instructive slides. Many more will occur to the keen student. What I have tried to do is to cover most of the techniques which are of wide application and can therefore be adapted for other subjects.

For many years I have had enormous pleasure from my (often fumbling) efforts to look into the wonderful world revealed by even a simple microscope. The blind alleys I have stumbled up and the mistakes I have made beggar description. I could find no simple book of reference as a guide. I found that professional biologists and teachers often tended to be cagey and less than helpful and perhaps a little impatient with the ignorant amateur. Frankly the most helpful and knowledgeable people I have come across have been laboratory technicians. They usually have great manipulative skill and are full of little tips of their own.

This little book is offered, therefore, in the hope that it will save the reader many hours of abortive trial and error and in the hope that it may lead to some of the enjoyment I have had.

Do not neglect to experiment however, and to try ideas of your own. Because I suggest a certain process or stain this does not mean that this is the only, or even the best, way. Try others.

I have not dealt specifically with photo micrography although it is clear from some illustrations that I use this. Anyone with a SLR camera can take photographs through his microscope. It requires no more than connecting his camera, minus lens, to the eyepiece tube of his microscope by means of some sort of light tight connection, either home made or a specially made adaptor obtainable in camera shops.

There are so many makes of cameras and microscopes that it did not seem practicable to give more than the vague advice of – "Get on and try it". You will not get first class micro photographs of course. These need an optical bench and special cameras and lighting set ups – all too expensive for the amateur and also beyond the scope of this book.

2. MICROSCOPES AND LENSES

HAND LENSES

I suppose most people have had experience of short-sighted friends who, when wanting to see fine detail, take off their spectacles and hold the object to be examined very close to the eye. Because of their sight defect they can focus fine detail at distances of only an inch or so. People with normal sight or 'long' sight cannot do this. For most people a distance of about 10 in. gives maximum clarity. Indeed, most of the older microscopes were based on this fact and had tube lengths of 10 in. Modern lenses permit the use of the more convenient tube length of about 6 in.

The purpose of all magnifying systems is to give the effect of bringing the object very close to the eye but still be in focus without giving eyestrain.

A lens, either plano-convex or convex on both sides, acts like a series of prisms and refracts rays of light from an object to a focal point on the other side of the lens. A concave mirror will produce much the same effect except that the focal point is on the same side as the object of course. There are other optical differences between lenses and mirrors which do not concern us here. In essence all magnifying systems – pocket magnifiers, telescopes, microscopes, camera lenses, etc. are developments of this simple function of lenses with refinements of more or less complexity.

The great disadvantage of a single lens is that, like a prism, light of different colours are refracted at slightly different angles so that their focal points do not coincide. Also the image formed is on a curved plane. The result of these two defects, or 'aberrations' as they are called, is that the magnified image is not sharp all over and will often be surrounded by coloured haloes.

The defects can be corrected by having, instead of a single lens, a combination of two or more lenses of flint and crown glass computed so that the different characteristics of one corrects those of the other. Most so-called 'aplanat' pocket magnifiers are made in this way.

For our purposes the short distance between object and lens is a further drawback. A hand lens, too, by definition, has to be held in one hand although it is true that a simple stand can be improvised by drilling small holes in the folding lens cover so that it can be slid up and down on a thin rod such as a knitting needle.

The magnifying power of a lens is found by dividing its focal length into the minimum distinct vision distance of 10 in. referred to above. Thus, the magnification of a lens of 1 in. focal length is 10/1 = ten times; a ½ in. lens would be 20 times and a 2 in. lens five times and so on.

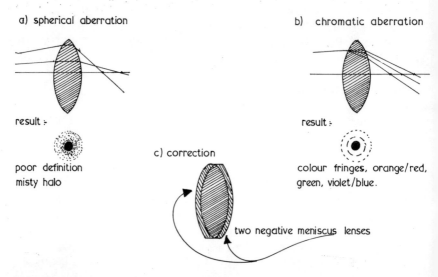

Fig. 1 Defects in single lenses.

(a) Light rays meeting a lens near its periphery strike the surface at a different angle from those nearer the centre and are consequently refracted differently. This gives rise to spherical aberration.

(b) Refraction through a dense transparent medium splits white light into its coloured constituents because each colour is refracted at a slightly different angle. This is chromatic aberration.

These defects can be corrected by assembling lens components of glass of different densities. The 'plus' characteristics of one can be made to offset the 'minus' characteristics of the other. Crown and flint glasses are often used for this purpose.

Fig. 2　A simple hand lens mounted on a rigid stand. This gives limited magnification but is useful for, say, acarine examination of bees for which the 'set up' in the photograph is arranged.

To recapitulate, the disadvantages of a single lens for the purpose of dissection are:

> The lens has to be fairly close to the eye.
>
> There is insufficient distance between the object and the eye to allow the use of tools.
>
> Marginal rays are refracted more than those nearer to the optical axis resulting in poor definition and a misty halo round the image (spherical aberration).
>
> If the lens is uncorrected, different colours are refracted unequally so that the image is surrounded by coloured fringes (chromatic aberration).
>
> The magnification is insufficient.

What we need is some system which will:

1. Give a magnification of about 30 diameters.
2. Have about 3 in. clearance between the dissection and the object lens.
3. Be mounted on a rigid, focussable stand.

4. Utilise corrected lenses, preferably but not essentially, changeable.
5. Have a simple focussing arrangement.
6. Give an erect image.

All these requirements are met by a prismatic erecting microscope.

DISSECTING MICROSCOPES

The old binocular low power microscopes made by such reliable firms as Leitz, Beck, Baker, etc. were excellent and their modern equivalents are as good – perhaps even better. Being binocular they give a stereoscopic image and therefore a '3D' effect; they are adjustable for inter-pupilliary distance and the eyepieces are usually inclined. The result is that they do not tire the eyes and are first-class tools to work with – but they are costly, even second-hand.

In recent years a number of firms have produced small monocular erecting instruments, sometimes made completely of plastic. These vary in quality and some are 'more equal than others'. Testing is advised before buying. However, it is not difficult to improvise a perfectly serviceable dissecting microscope either from field glasses as a temporary hook up or, even better, to make up a microscope from odds and ends to be kept solely for dissecting. I think this is the best plan.

The important thing is to utilise the materials which come readily to hand or which can be bought cheaply. The following methods are suggestions only, to be varied according to the reader's skill and ingenuity. I have tried them all and made sure that they will work.

Field Glasses with a Supplementary Lens

Field glasses, either binocular or monocular, are used to look at objects at a distance and are not capable of being focusssed on objects close by – i.e. they are computed to deal with parallel rays.

If an object is placed at the focal point of a lens, emerging rays will be parallel (Fig. 3). This principle can be utilised with one side of a pair of binoculars (Fig. 4). Fasten a lens close to the field lens of the glasses and this will permit objects a few inches away to be brought into sharp focus. Interpose a cardboard stop between lens and binoculars. A piece of card with a $\frac{1}{4}$ in. circular hole will do. By cutting out the marginal rays this will increase the depth of focus and brighten up the image. A suitable stand could be a baseboard of $\frac{3}{4}$ in. timber in which a short length of $\frac{3}{8}$ in. dowel rod has been fixed vertically. Make a cradle of sheet aluminium or similar metal sheet in which the binoculars can rest. Fasten a $\frac{1}{4}$ in. bolt to the cradle. The whole is secured to the dowel rod by means of a retort clamp which will give easy up and down movement.

The neatest way of securing the supplementary lens and stop to the field glasses is to make a paper tube which is a tight fit on the binoculars and to fix the supplementary lens and stop to one end of the tube. It is most unlikely that you will find a lens the exact diameter of the binocular field lens so a little packing will probably be needed.

Try using the projection lens from your slide projector as your supplementary lens. This makes a rather clumsy set-up but definition will be better than using a single lens.

At the experimental 'mock-up' stage I find that three strips of Blue Tack or masking tape will hold the lens and stop quite securely while trials of distances, etc. are made.

After getting the height about right by sliding the retort clamp up or down the rod, final focussing can be done with the normal focussing wheel of the binocular.

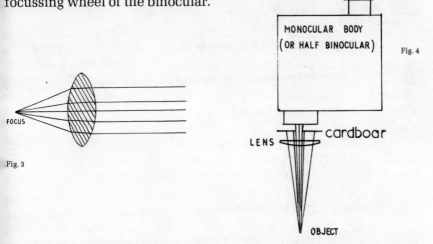

Figs. 3 and 4   The lens systems of field glasses, either monocular or binocular, are computed to accept parallel rays from distant objects and bring them to a focus close behind the eye lens just as a single lens might do (Fig. 3).

By placing a 'weak' lens in front of the field lens its characteristics are altered. Instead of focussing on distant objects the field glasses now bring close objects into focus (Fig. 4).

11

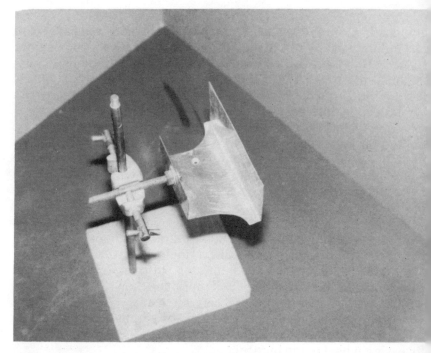

Fig. 5 Simple sheet metal cradle for holding binoculars or a monocular for temporary conversion to use as a dissecting microscope.

Low power field glasses are best. A field glass with a power of X6 with a supplementary lens of 3 in. focus will give a magnification of about X20 and will give ample room below the lens for dissecting or examination. High power field glasses are less suitable – they have to be raised at an inconvenient height from the bench.

All the above considerations apply equally to a monocular which will be much lighter and neater. There are some cheap all-plastic monoculars on the market which might be adapted.

Purpose-built Dissecting Microscopes

The suggestions made so far are really little more than 'hook-ups'. They are useful for occasional use but for serious and more prolonged work something more stable is needed. A low power erecting microscope kept solely for dissection is well worth having and construction of such an instrument is well within the capabilities of the average handyman who can use simple tools.

12

. Using a half-binocular

A logical development from using a broken half binocular or a prismatic monocular is to discard the field and eye lenses, retaining the primatic element whose only purpose is to erect the image. It is sometimes possible to pick up a broken pair of binoculars with the possibility of salvaging the prismatic part.)

The field lens is replaced by a 2 in. microscope objective and the eye lens by a microscope eyepiece of about six times magnification. This will give a working distance of some 2 to $2\frac{1}{2}$ in. between objective and dissection. The field of view just about covers the abdomen of the worker honeybee. The magnification is about 30 times. More than this makes working with instruments increasingly difficult. A 3 in. objective will give a magnification of about 20 times and a working distance of 3 to $3\frac{1}{2}$ in.

Most compound microscopes seem to be fitted out with ten times and 15 times eyepieces. The lower of these is quite suitable if you do not want the expense of getting a special six times eyepiece for your dissector.

Make a tube of rolled and glued brown paper ('Kraft' quality is good) with a bore so that the eyepiece can be dropped in loosely. Glue this to the orifice where you have removed the eyelens from the half binocular. A similar tube but shorter and which will give a *tight* fit to the microscope objective is glued to the field lens end. Modern adhesives are strong enough for this. I like one of the two-solution super epoxy resin types. These make a very strong joint, adhere well to metal especially if it is roughed up a little, set fairly quickly and dry water white. Araldite will do but dries with a characteristic 'horny' appearance.

A better arrangement if you can obtain one of the old brass microscope objective boxes is to cut out the centre of the lid with a piercing saw – or drill out a $\frac{3}{8}$ in. hole – and file the hole out smoothly almost to the female objective thread which used to be cut into the lids of these boxes. Solder or glue to the field lens end of the half binocular. You will then have a thread into which you can screw an objective of any desired power. You will have rigidity and inter-changeability.

2. Assembly from basics

If a half binocular or a monocular is not available it is by no means difficult to assemble your own prism box. I originally did this in

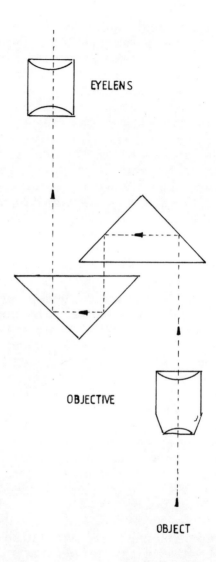

EYELENS

OBJECTIVE

OBJECT

Fig. 6 Erection of image by prisms. During the passage from object to eye the image produced by a microscope is inverted and also reversed from left to right. By interposing two prisms between the objective and the eyelens the light rays are caused to be reflected from four internal surfaces of the prisms. This erects the image both ways. In practice, the prisms are held at right angles to each other. The sketch shows them in the same plane for the sake of clarity.

14

Fig. 7   Older type objective and brass carrying box. Often these boxes had, inside the screw 'lid', a female microscope objective thread.

both metal and wood. I have to confess that the results were a little clumsy but both kinds worked satisfactorily – and this is surely the ultimate test.

Your first need is to obtain two right angle prisms. Many optical instruments like binoculars utilise a Swan Cube which is simply two prisms cemented together. So much the better if you can get one. Mounting one piece of glass is easier than mounting two.

For a metal box use a washed food tin. My first effort was a small baked bean tin but size will depend on the dimensions of your prisms. It will be easier, and neater, if your box is as small as may be, compatible with the size of the prisms. Mount these as indicated in Fig. 6, but at right angles to each other. A wooden box made of 3 mm ply, pinned and glued, can be made to the size needed.

Support for the prisms can be either two discs with holes at strategic places •to support the prisms or transverse strips of metal or wood across the inside of the box. The prisms *can* be secured to the discs and/or strips by epoxy resin adhesive. This will make a permanent fixture, but I think it is preferable to fit small clips made of strips cut from the ubiquitous food tin. You are then free to change your mind from time to time and to make alterations to your masterpiece – a fairly common occurrence I find.

Fitment for the objective and eyepiece are as already described. Paint the inside of the prism box with matt black paint.

15

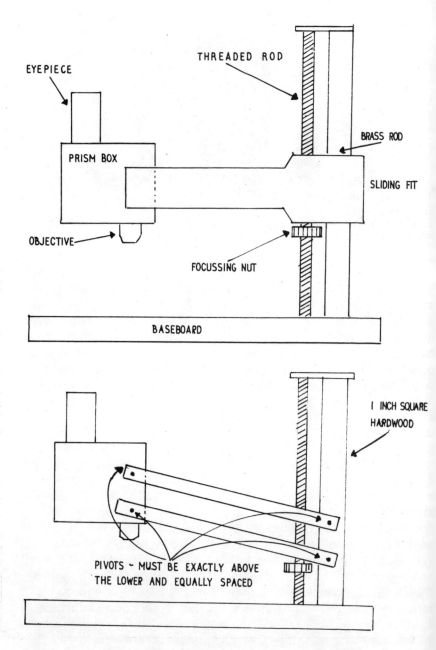

EYEPIECE

THREADED ROD

PRISM BOX

BRASS ROD

SLIDING FIT

OBJECTIVE

FOCUSSING NUT

BASEBOARD

I INCH SQUARE
HARDWOOD

PIVOTS - MUST BE EXACTLY ABOVE
THE LOWER AND EQUALLY SPACED

Fig. 8   Two suggested arrangements for home-made dissecting microscopes.

16

3. The 'ah that might be useful' method

I have to confess that I am an inveterate 'poker about' on junk stalls and in Army surplus stores. Over the years I have acquired a stock of (to me) useful items of ephemera which I regard as valuable and my wife regards as dust-gathering rubbish best consigned to the council tip. In our present context it might be profitable for me to describe my own dissecting microscope, which has been in fairly constant use for more years than I care to remember. It is entirely satisfactory, the optics leave little to be desired and has the dual advantages of being simple and cheap to construct and extremely flexible. Its only drawback is that it is monocular. I think that a *good* binocular instrument would, perhaps, be less tiring to use, but even this is arguable – and a poor binocular is worse than useless.

The main components come from stalls in a well known London street market.

The barrel part was, to the best of my belief, a sighting telescope taken from an ancient artillery piece. It had a very low magnification, field and eye lenses, of course, cross wires and a small and very neat erecting prismatic system. The last bit was what I wanted. It is now a long time ago but I think I paid five shillings for it (if anyone remembers what a shilling was). Another stall at a different time yielded the smashed front end of a Victorian magic lantern. The part of this which interested me was the focussing part of the projection lens. The lens itself was cracked so apparently 'useless'. This had a friction movement of about 2 in. in and out and a small rack and pinion device giving another 1¼ in. of movement.

From the sighting telescope I removed the field lens, the eye lens and the cross wires. I filed out the upper end to take a standard microscope eyepiece and to the lower end soldered a drilled and filed lid from a brass microscope objective box.

The final result has been an adaptable and versatile dissecting microscope which has given me many years of service (Fig. 9).

For anyone at all interested in the DIY aspect of microscopy I cannot over-emphasise the advantages to be gained from browsing in the many surplus stores and 'junk' stalls in street markets. It is *always* a good idea to keep odd bits of impedimenta on the principle that they 'might come in useful' one day. They always do.

Fig. 9   DIY erecting prismatic microscope for dissecting with high intensity lamp.

BASEBOARDS FOR HOME-MADE MICROSCOPES

The Stand or Base

You are likely to be working with your microscope on dissections
for fairly prolonged periods so it is worthwhile giving a little

thought to comfort and convenience. The first consideration must be the size of the base.

A great deal of your dissecting work will be carried out in small dissecting pans as described in another section. Let us assume that these will be about 3 in. in diameter. You will need to rest the sides of your hands on the baseboard in order to hold the pan and also to work with your instruments. This means that your base will need to be at least 9 in. square. Precise dimensions are not critical so long as they are not less than 9 in. In a way, the bigger the better, except that the question of clumsiness soon arises.

Domestic tables are customarily some 6 in. or so lower than the height of laboratory benches so it is a help to raise your base by side pieces. Two inches makes all the difference.

By raising the base in this way you will also give yourself the opportunity of arranging for transmitted light. Although most of your work will need incident light, there are many occasions when transmitted light will be most useful – for instance, when arranging specimens for permanent mounting on microslides. Drill a hole 1 in. or 1½ in. in diameter in your base making sure that its centre coincides with the centre of vision of your microscope when mounted. A mirror below the base is neither necessary nor desirable. At the low magnifications you will be using, a piece of white card at an angle of 45° is quite adequate. I made a simple clip out of sheet zinc which I screwed below the hole and which holds a white card. I fitted into the hole a circle of ⅛ in. perspex. A thin smear of synthetic glue round the rim made it a waterproof fixture.

Focussing Devices

The baseboard will also carry your focussing arrangement, another reason for not making it too flimsy. Fig. 9 shows my own magic lantern focussing mount screwed to the base of my microscope. I soldered a disc of brass to the top of the lens mount and to this soldered two brass strips which, in turn, are drilled and screwed to the barrel of the microscope.

In the case of monocular adaptions or made-up prism boxes the anchorage could be via a metal rod fixed vertically and firmly in the baseboard with a parallel threaded rod bearing a nut for focussing adjustment. Screwing the nut up or down will obviously focus the microscope (see Fig. 8).

An alternative arrangement which I have tried and found satisfactory is two parallel brass strips pivoted to the prism box and to a 1 in. square piece of hardwood glued and screwed to the base. Again, a threaded rod gives the up and down movement needed (Fig. 8).

There are many variations on this theme depending on the materials available.

LIGHTING FOR DISSECTING MICROSCOPES

The illumination available at any given point varies inversely with the square of the distance from the light source and also, if viewed through any magnifying device, inversely with the square of the magnification.

It is clear then that what we need is an intense source of light which can be focussed on our specimen. I have found the most satisfactory way of doing this is to use a 40 watt car headlight bulb of the old type powered through the mains via a 6- or 12-volt transformer according to the type of bulb. The old type bulbs with a double contact, fit standard SBC lamp holders.

The light can be concentrated by means of a lens or a concave mirror. A mirror of about 3 in. in diameter is lighter than a lens of the same size and is simpler to fix and ample ventilation is easier to arrange in order to avoid overheating. A lens or mirror of about this size is needed so as to have a reasonable 'light grasp'. My own mirror is from an old pre-1914 Aldis signalling lamp I used in 'Dad's Army' days. For signalling purposes this was one stage better than smoke signals, but surprisingly effective. It is fortunate that our Morse was so primitive that the rather rude messages which used to flash across the Essex countryside could be understood only by a tight knit group of well meaning fumblers.

Fig. 10 demonstrates the method of construction. If possible arrange things so that the distance between bulb and mirror can be varied a little so that the light can be focussed on the specimen. What is needed is a slightly out of focus image of the lamp filament in the same plane as the specimen. This will given an intense pool of light.

If the lamp is supported about 10 in. above the work table, the light can be made to shine downwards at an angle of about 45° and avoid unpleasant reflections from the dissecting dish. A metal rod (or a short length of dowel) fixed firmly in a wooden base with

Fig. 10   Home-made lamp for dissecting. A 40 watt car headlamp bulb runs from a trans-ormer with a 4 in. concave mirror to concentrate the light.

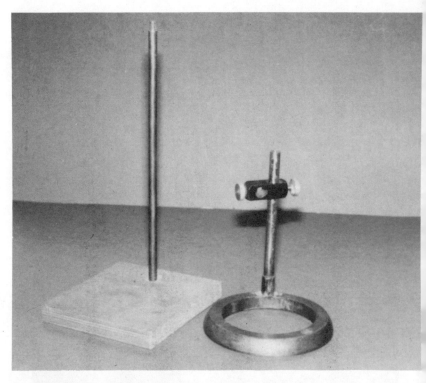

Fig. 11 Improvised stands to carry lamps, etc. Left, 12 mm wooden base with length o꞉ curtain rod. Right, brass ring with brass rod soldered to rim. Note adjustable clamp.

some kind of clip, such as a retort clamp running up and down, i꞉ all that is needed. Accurate focussing is not wanted. Attach ɑ 'hood' of sheet aluminium or thin sheet metal (food tin again?) to prevent the light shining into your eyes.

I originally made my lamp stand integral with the dissecting microscope stand but found this inflexible and unsatisfactory. A separate stand is much better and the range of adjustment wider It can have its uses in photography too.

Finishing

If you feel you *must* smarten up your products do not use glos꞉ paint. Shiny surfaces can be a nuisance. I am usually eager to ge on and put my things to practical use and rarely bother to pain them. However, I can see that they would look much more profes sional if I did. This question of avoiding glossy finishes applies to

ll the home-made articles described in this book. Always use
black matt or crackle finish. Unwanted reflections are anathema
n optics.

MICROSCOPES

BUYING A DISSECTING MICROSCOPE

An erecting prismatic microscope is an essential tool for anatomi-
al dissections of insects and for the preparation of specimens for
permanent mounting. I have already given in this book hints for
the home construction of an instrument which will fulfill our
main requirements, which are:

1. An erect image.
2. Magnification of about 30 times.
3. A working distance of at *least* 2 in. between specimen and
   objective – 3 in. is even better.
4. A stage large enough to support a dissecting pan and also
   provide resting places for the hands.
5. An intense light source which can be focussed and is
   capable of adjustment as to height and distance.

In recent years there has been quite a spate of instruments
oming on the market, some from behind the iron and bamboo
urtains. Some are excellent but some fall far short of our require-
ents under headings 2, 4 and 5 above. In particular the poor little
pencil light' battery torches are quite useless and are best
emoved.

If you are thinking of buying a dissecting microscope, and this
s an admirable idea, please make sure that it is capable of doing
what you want it to. An inferior instrument will only lead to
rustration and disappointment.

COMPOUND MICROSCOPES

These, too, are essential tools for the beekeeper and the naturalist.
t is a waste of money and effort to buy an instrument far beyond
ne's probable needs when a simpler microscope will do all that is
eeded just as efficiently and much more easily. However, an
indifferent instrument will only result in disappointment and
iscouragement.

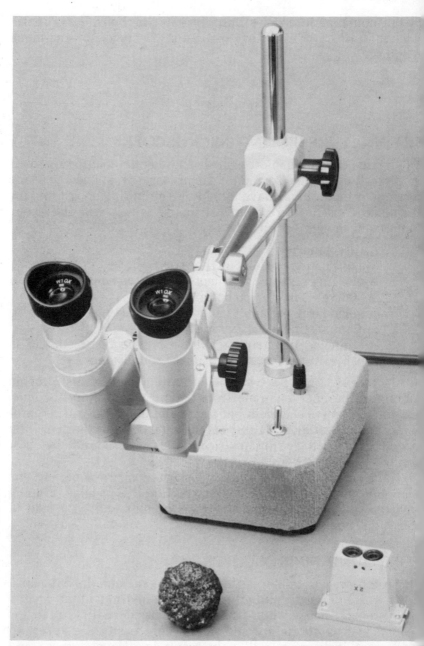

Fig. 12 There are many excellent binocular prismatic dissecting microscopes on the market. This is one example.

24

SECOND-HAND MICROSCOPES

There is always a plentiful supply of second-hand microscopes available. The problem is to sort the wheat from the chaff. I think two extremes are to be avoided. Never buy a second-hand microscope merely because it is cheap nor because it is impressive, elaborate and has a large number of 'accessories'. Most of these latter are likely to be obsolete and worthless. The only really safe thing to do is to enlist the help of someone who is familiar with microscopes and has used them as tools.

The optical components of older instruments should be regarded with some caution. The cement between the components of objectives (often Canada balsam) may have become crystallised or contain bubbles. They may have been dropped or otherwise subjected to stress and as a result be out of alignment.

Make quite sure that the nosepiece thread and the eyepiece are standard sizes. An old stand in good condition can be fitted with modern lenses *provided the threads are standard*. Older instruments by Ross, Powell and Lealand, Beck and Crouch are likely to be very satisfactory provided there are no obvious signs of physical damage. Indeed, microscopes by Ross and Powell and Lealand particularly are outstanding – but they are expensive. They were built by craftsmen and the workmanship has never been equalled. There is only one caveat. Modern objectives are usually computed for use with 160 mm body tubes. Some of the older instruments were made with 10 in. tubes. Some older eyepieces are not to be despised. Often they have a wider field than modern eyepieces and the exit pupil is a little larger and the eyepoint farther away from the lens. These factors make for comfort.

With the exception of Powell and Lealand high power objectives I do not think that older lenses of a higher power than ¼ in. are worth having.

It is probably safe never to buy a second-hand microscope that does not bear the makers' name – and a recognisable one at that!

Testing a Second-hand Microscope

1. The thread on the nosepiece *must* be standard. Try to fit a modern objective. If it will not fit the deal is off.
2. Test for stability. Incline the body to the horizontal position. It should show no tendency to tip over.

3. Test all adjustments for smoothness and lack of backlash. You should be able to focus a 40 x objective with the coarse focus adjustment only. It should be possible to move the fine focus adjustment an appreciable amount before the image goes noticeably out of focus. Return the fine focus to its original position and the focus should be restored exactly.
4. Test rigidity of the stage by noticing if gentle pressure on it puts the object out of focus and if removal of pressure restores focus. Test body tube for rigidity by slight transverse pressure.
5. Examine the focussing and centring adjustments of the substage. The best instruments have rack and pinion focussing, but many 'students' instruments have an Abbe condenser fitted as a sliding fit in a substage tube. The rack and pinion arrangement is very much to be preferred but the 'students' type can be quite adequate except for the most critical work.
6. The mirror should have a plane and a concave side. Both should be free of flaws and blemishes.
7. Carefully examine the front component of any high power objective (¼ in. and upwards) for scratches and polish. Have a look at the metal mount too for any signs of discolouration, scratch or other misuse.
8. Finally, examine a slide with which you are familiar under all available objectives. The immediate appearance will indicate whether the objective is a good one or not.

Buying a New Microscope

When buying a new instrument none of the horrors listed in the 'second-hand' section need be feared. My experience has been that all manufacturers and most retailers are usually helpful and if told the prospective buyers' needs, will advise as to the best type of microscope suited to those needs.

Prices vary greatly and on the whole I think it is fair to say 'you gets what you pays for'. Try to get a simple, soundly designed, stand so that it can be added to later on when more elaborate refinements are wanted. Many of the so-called 'students' outfits are excellent.

Do not forget to have a look at some of the imported microscopes. It is sad to have to note that many of the Russian, Japanese

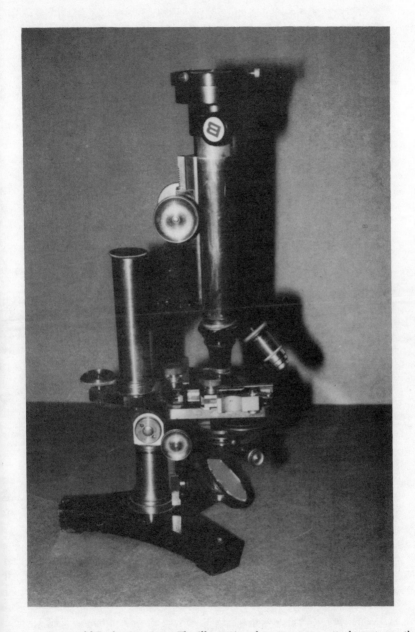

Fig. 13   A very old Beck microscope. The illustration shows a camera attachment over the eyepiece for photomicrography. This microscope has given the writer many years of excellent service and is nowhere near the end of its useful life.

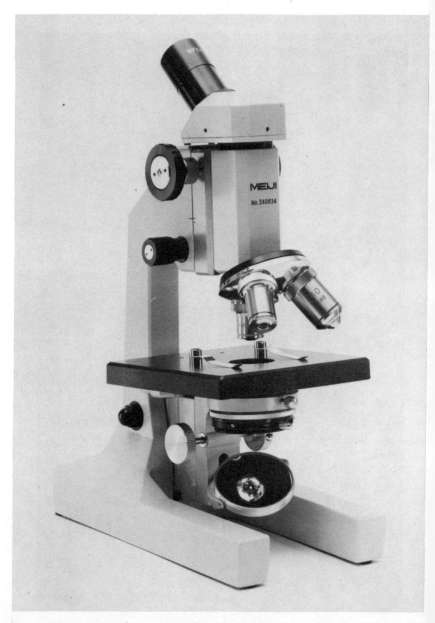

Fig. 14 Many very good microscopes from the Soviet Union and the Far East are now available. Often their optical performance is first class, but finish may perhaps leave something to be desired. They are always considerably cheaper than the comparable English-made instrument.

28

and Chinese models now available are at worst the equal and in some cases superior to the nationally-made articles and sell at very competitive prices.

A Microscope Lamp

In most biology teaching laboratories the routine microscope lamps available consist of open-ended metal lamp shades about 4 in. or 5 in. in diameter adjustable as to height by means of a sliding clamp on a retort stand. The more sophisticated, if that is the right word, have a kind of lid over the open end with a hole in it. This is not the best arrangement. The light source is too large, giving rise to glare and flare and the light intensity cannot be varied.

Research people often use a low voltage lamp powered via a transformer. The light source is a small filament in one plane and in some cases can be a single tiny incandescent ball giving, in effect, a point source. These lamps are fitted with filter holders, lenses for focussing and an iris diaphragm for controlling intensity – or even a rheostat across the transformer for the same purpose. These lamps are costly.

A compromise between these two extremes would be suitable for us and can be easily made up at home. The ubiquitous food tin (minus label, of course) forms a lamp holder and shade. Cut a hole in the bottom of the tin of sufficient size to take a standard lamp holder and drill a number of $\frac{1}{4}$ in. holes round the sides of the tin for ventilation. At this point it might be advisable to point out the prudence of using three-core cable in all your home-made apparatus using a mains supply. Earth the body of your apparatus and use a three-pin plug. Cut and fix a disc of wood (3 mm ply) into the open end of the tin and secure with two small round-headed screws driven in from the sides. In the centre of the disc cut a 1 in. hole with brace and bit. On the outside face of the disc mount three clips of either sheet metal or wood strips on each side of and below the 1 in. hole so that 2 in. filters or squares of sheet metal may be dropped in. Cut a few 2 in. squares of sheet metal and in the centre of each drill holes of varying sizes. In this way you will be able to change the size of your light source at will – merely by changing the square in use.

Most microscope objectives are computed for blue/green light and *all* older objectives are. The use of a blue/green transparent filter will slightly improve the working of your high power objectives and, at the same time, be less tiring to the eyes.

A $\frac{1}{4}$ in. bolt secured through the side of the tin and held tight by a nut will provide anchorage on a retort stand and clamp or a similar stand of your own making.

The intensity of the light may be controlled by a dimmer switch (q.v.), but a word of caution is needed here. As the light is dimmed it becomes more and more yellow. This is acceptable for visual examination but in photomicrography will give an unpleasant overall orange cast with colour film. All tungsten lighting is, of course, yellowish. A blue filter will correct this to some extent and give an approximation to daylight.

SETTING UP A COMPOUND MICROSCOPE

Having acquired your microscope it is worth while spending a little time and trouble setting it up properly. If this is done, the image will be crisp and the details clearly discernible.

Screw the objectives into the revolving nosepiece so that when the nosepiece is turned in a clockwise direction when viewed from above, progressively higher powers will come into the axis of the microscope.

Place an eyepiece in the eyepiece tube. If you have a number of eyepieces start with the ten times (marked X10).

Incline the microscope to a convenient angle for viewing. Many modern instruments are now made with the stage horizontal, but the eyepiece tube permanently inclined so that there is no adjustment possible as to angle.

Place your lamp about 8 in. away from the mirror which should have the plane side turned towards the lamp. Use an opal or a frosted bulb in the lamp and adjust it so that it is shining directly at the mirror.

Turn the low power objective into the axis. This will be marked X10, or if it is an older lens, $\frac{2}{3}$ in. Focus the substage condenser to bring the image of the light source in focus superimposed on the image of the specimen, which should also be focussed of course. It is not always easy to see if the light source is in focus and I find it helpful to hold something with a sharp point – a pencil, for instance – against the light bulb and to focus this. Adjust the mirror until the light source is brought centrally into the field of view. If the lamp has an iris diaphragm close it until the light source only just fills the field of view.

Remove the eyepiece and look down the tube. Close the sub-stage iris until the back of the objective is almost but not quite filled with light. Replace the eyepiece and swing the X40 objective into axis. Close the lamp iris a little more until, once again, the field of view is only just filled with light. Remove the eyepiece and close the substage iris until the back of the objective is no more than two-thirds filled. This will give a setting of good contrast and resolution. Opening the substage iris will improve resolution at the expense of contrast and closing it will improve contrast and depth of focus at the expense of resolution.

If an oil immersion objective is to be used (usually marked X100 and has a red ring round the mount in modern lenses), locate and centralise the object to be examined with the X10 and X40 objectives. Rack the microscope up and swing the oil immersion lens into position. Place a drop of oil on the specimen. This *must* be proper immersion oil sold for the purpose.

With the coarse adjustment rack down very slowly until the objective nearly touches the cover slip and the drop of oil fills the space between objective and cover slip. Focus slowly upwards until the image comes into view. It may do so quickly. Finally, focus precisely with the fine adjustment. You may find that the image improves slightly if the substage iris is opened. This is because the Abbe condenser, which you are most likely to have, is uncorrected and suffers from spherical aberration. This has no deleterious effect on the type of work we are considering; how-ever, if much work of a critical nature with the highest powers is to be done an achromatic condenser would be very desirable. It is likely to be expensive and will need careful focussing and centring.

Are You Sitting Comfortably?

It adds a great deal to your pleasure and to the efficiency with which you work if you are not subjected to physical discomfort.

Your chair should be of such a height that both feet will rest flat on the floor and at the same time your table or work bench is at comfortable writing height. Having achieved this comfortable pose you may well find, as I did, that the microscope eyepiece is a little too low so that prolonged work produces a crick in the neck. This was certainly the case with my own work table. My micro-scope needed to be raised about 4 in. and if this were not done, the advantage of having an inclined eyepiece tube would be lost.

A simple wooden box was the obvious answer, but an empty box serving no purpose other than to raise the microscope went against the grain. In any case would I not have to raise the lamp too?

In the end I made my box to carry out three functions – to give a firm raised base for the microscope, to replace my lamp with built-in illumination, and to provide a storage drawer for spare eyepieces, objectives, filters, immersion oil, etc.

I made my box from scrap 12 mm ply, 23 cm by 18 cm and 8 cm deep. It has no bottom. I drilled a ¾ in. hole in the top of the box equidistant from the two long sides and roughly under the axis of the microscope when this was placed on the box. Underneath I fixed an SBC lampholder (earthed) holding a 25 watt 'candle' lamp with the filament as nearly as I could judge under the axis and with a switch incorporated in the circuit.

I cut a piece of 3 mm ply just a little larger than the box and from the centre removed a cut-out exactly the shape of the microscope foot. The box needs ventilation when the lamp is lit and I found that a series of ¼ in. holes drilled round the upper edge of the front and the front end of the sides looked after this. I cut a piece of aluminium sheet (thickness not important) about 2 cm square and in the middle drilled a smallish hole. This aluminium sheet is to be fixed over the ¾ in. hole in the top of the box to restrict the amount of light coming-into the substage condenser. I found that a 9 mm hole will fill the field of view about ⅞ths with light. The best size to suit your set up is only to be found by trial and error.

I think the iris diaphragm from an old disused camera would be an improvement but, so far, my local 'junk' shops have not produced one.

The mirror and gimbal was removed from the microscope and stored away safely in the little accessory drawer.

Now comes the question of alignment. This is absolutely vital but not hard to achieve. With the lamp switched on I assembled all the parts I had made (nothing had been fixed so far except the lamp so the lamp was my datum line). I placed the microscope on the box and focussed a slide using the X10 objective. It was now easy for me to move the aluminium sheet with hole and the microscope. I made several checks, focussing down on the hole and, finally, when I was quite sure that all was exactly in line, I fastened the 3 mm ply microscope foot holder to the top of the box

Fig. 15 Raising the level of the microscope and installing built-in illumination. Top left, finished set up. Bottom, underneath of box to show candle lamp. Top right, top of box; cut-out to hold microscope foot in position and drawer to hold spare accessories.

with glue and pins and trimmed up the edges for neatness. The aluminium sheet was fastened to the box top with a single screw so that it can be swung aside if necessary.

I dislike the yellow colour of tungsten lighting and always use a light blue filter in the filter holder of my substage condenser. To deepen this a little I fixed a further blue filter over what has now become the light orifice with three small dabs of clear epoxy resin glue.

As a result of this arrangement I no longer have to re-align and re-focus my lamp every time the microscope is wanted and it is flexible. Lamps of higher wattage can be easily inserted and a domestic dimmer switch incorporated in the circuit. But care is needed here. The more the light is dimmed the yellower it becomes. This is bad for microphotography. Personally I leave the outfit permanently set up in this way and use a large polythene bag as a dust cover. The microscope box is only used for transporting.

3. ANCILLARY APPARATUS

AN EMBEDDING OVEN

When embedding tissues in paraffin wax prior to sectioning, it is important not to overheat the wax otherwise the tissues will be subject to shrinking and will literally be cooked. Best results are obtained when the wax is only fractionally hotter than its melting point and no more. This situation is obtained by installing the heat source above the wax container and adjusting it so that the top half of the wax is molten while the bottom half remains cool and solid. In these conditions the tissues to be infiltrated sink down through the molten wax and come to rest on the surface of the unmelted wax and are thus kept at just the right temperature.

I am indebted to Mr T. J. Maxwell for his permission to describe below his method of constructing an embedding oven. I have used one constructed on these lines for some time and have found it satisfactory. It is reliable and very considerably cheaper than the professional article, which may be water-jacketted and thermostatically controlled.

The oven functions by reflecting heat from a 40 watt domestic light bulb downwards on to a wax container. Provision is made in my own for varying the height of the shelf. Possibly the addition of a few ventilation holes could be made to reduce heat if this is found desirable. Under working conditions the shelf is raised or lowered until the wax in the container is melted to about half its depth.

Construction (see illustration) is of one inch deal or block-board. I think the latter is best as no problems of warping under heat arise. Internal dimensions are 9 in. by 5 in. by 5 in. The heat reflector is cut from a fruit tin opened into a U shape and held free of the top and sides by metal washers. The lamp holder is fitted through a hole drilled in the back and surrounded by another tin reflector as is the top half of the door. Make sure that this fits tightly to avoid heat loss and secure it with a cabinet hook fastener. Cut a square opening in the bottom half of the door and double glaze this. It is a good idea to keep an eye on the wax container during the infiltration process.

The shelf can be either of perforated zinc on a wood frame or better still a square of strong wire mesh, which I prefer.

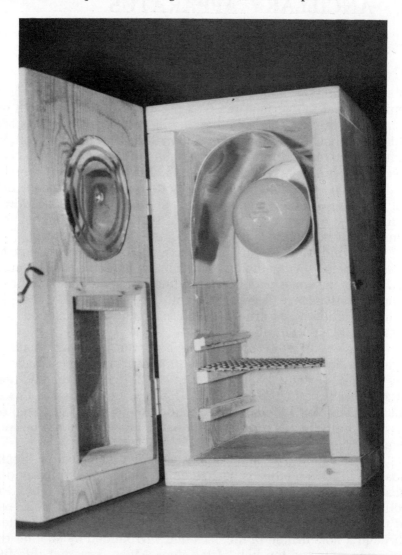

Fig. 16   An electric embedding oven made almost entirely from scrap material.

Mr Maxwell recommends the fitting of a thermostat in the circuit. This is a safe and useful refinement but I have not found it really necessary.

Lowering the shelf has given me all the heat control I have needed. Ventilation holes and a lower wattage lamp are fall-backs if needed.

MICROTOMES
A HAND MICROTOME

A Microtome is a device for cutting very thin slices from previously prepared specimens, sometimes by hand and sometimes by a mechanical aid. We will consider the hand microtome first.

The specimen is held in a recess and is pushed upwards by small degrees towards a flat plate across which a razor is drawn by hand. Much depends on the skill of the operator. A serviceable microtome may be improvised from a discarded outlet pipe from a hand basin or bath. The normal cross-piece in the outlet is cut out and the interior filed smooth. A specimen holder is made from hard wood and should be a close fit in the pipe – close enough to allow the smallest possible side play but free enough to allow unimpeded up and down movements.

The retaining nut and the thread on the outside of the pipe can be adapted to give an advance movement to a specimen fixed to the top of the holder.

The top of the flange should be rubbed down to a smooth surface with 'Wet and Dry' paper so that a razor can be drawn evenly across the surface. Sections so cut tend to be rather thick because the advance mechanism is coarse. I found that good sections could not be expected at every cut and certainly it is not possible to get serial sections in ribbon form.

In spite of the disadvantages this is a good method of introduction into the art of section cutting and much can be learned from the inevitable mistakes.

A ROCKING MICROTOME

At one time I was able to use a Cambridge Rocking Microtome in a well equipped laboratory. The pleasure of producing good sections of pre-determined thickness at almost every stroke and, if needed, in serial form was such an advance on the hand held variety that I was encouraged to try to make one of my own. I could not afford the professional article and in any event cutting sections was (and still is) a small part of my anatomical studies so that the expense would not have been justified.

What follows is my version of the Cambridge Rocking Microtome. It invariably provokes politely concealed titters from my friends but it has given me many years of service. I was happy too, to do a little repetitive research work for the late Mr G. Clout, a man I greatly admired. Mr Clout was working on Nosema disease at the time and asked if I could produce large numbers of cross-sections of the small gut of worker honeybees and to search for abnormalities in them. I cannot say that I made any revolutionary discoveries but in any form of research a negative finding is sometimes of value.

The principle of the Cambridge rocker is simplicity itself. Like many other occasions it is carrying out the principles into practice and making a functional piece of apparatus that give rise to difficulties. The knife is fixed and sections are cut by moving the specimen up and down across the cutting edge. The fulcrum on which the specimen carrying arm is moved is itself pivoted in such a way that it can be tilted by tiny amounts and thus advance the specimen towards the knife. A strong spring operates the specimen arm ensuring that even and equal pressure is applied to all cuts. It is arranged so that specimens are advanced automatically and the cutting movement initiated by the simple pulling and release of a handle.

Particulars of my own machine follow. I have gone into some detail but I feel sure that readers will be able to improve on these in the light of the materials available to them. I think the important things are – to bear the principles involved always in mind, to aim for rigidity and the least possible backlash or play in the moving parts and to regard the measurements I have quoted as provisional: what is important is their inter-relationships, not the actual dimensions. The figures I use have been satisfactory for me and the materials at my disposal but could easily be varied.

THE BASE

The base consists of a rectangle of 15 mm multi-ply 40 × 18 cms. About 11 cms from the lefthand end a block of hardwood of pyrimadial shape 8 cms high is firmly glued and screwed. The top of the pyramid is truncated to give me a square platform 4 cms

A

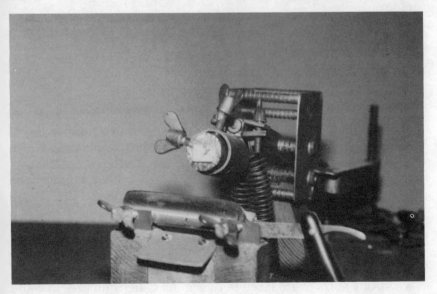

B

Fig. 17   Rocking microtome. A, general view: B, closer view of cutting knife, brass box and specimen holder.

each way. This bears the pivot so it is worth while making it good and strong.

THE PIVOTING MECHANISM

In my case this is the carcase of an old alarm clock with the 'works' removed but with the corner pillars left in situ.

Across the bottom of the box I fixed a rod which moves freely in the sides of the box and is secured by retaining nuts on the outside, making sure that there is as little lateral movement as possible. The rod is screwed firmly to the pyramidial hardwood block.

A piece of brass channel (arm A) 21 cm long is soldered to the box near its lower edge. 2 cms above the lower pivot and immediately perpendicular to it a further rod is fixed across the box. This must be left to move freely in its bearing holes and secured by external retaining nuts, again limiting lateral movement. Another piece of brass channel 33 cms long (arm B) is soldered to the top rod in such a way that about 6 cms or so projects to the left of the box. This short end will carry the specimen holder.

SPECIMEN HOLDER

A chuck to hold the wax embedded specimens is made from two pieces of brass tube 4 cms long, one small enough to move comfortably within the other. The larger tube is secured to the short end of arm B by a simple ball and socket joint capable of being tightened by a wing nut. The smaller (inner) tube has a piece of brass soldered to one end to close it. This is cross-hatched with an Eclipse saw blade to provide a 'key' for the attachment of the wax specimen block. It is held at the desired position in the outer tube by two thumb screws. Holes were drilled and tapped 2 BA. This in and out movement of the inner tube and the articulation of the ball joint makes it easy to align the wax block to the knife edge.

OPERATING SPRINGS

Two strong springs are fixed between the chuck end of arm B and the baseboard under slight tension. This keeps the chuck and specimen below the edge of the knife until the machine is operated.

KNIFE HOLDER

A block of hardwood is glued and screwed firmly to the lefthand edge of the baseboard. To the top of this are screwed two short pieces of brass channel. 2 cms is ample. Each is drilled and tapped to take wing nuts on short screwed rods to hold the knife firmly on its back with the cutting edge upwards. I found it simpler to standardise all my holes and screwed rods to 2 BA.

OPERATING ARM

A piece of cord is knotted through a hole in the righthand end of arm B. The cord passes through a staple partially driven into the baseboard immediately below the arm and the other end is secured to a brass handle 12 cms by 3 cms. This needs to be fairly stout. Mine was cut from 4 mm brass sheet. The handle is pivoted with the advance mechanism.

ADVANCE MECHANISM

It will be clear from the above description, the sketches and the photographs, that swinging the handle towards the operator through about 90° will cause arm B to move on its pivot bringing the specimen chuck up above the knife. Releasing the handle will allow the springs to bring the specimen down across the knife. Raising arm A in small distances will tilt the box to which it is soldered and so bring the specimen ever closer to the knife for subsequent cutting strokes.

A brass bush is fixed into the base. In this runs a steel rod, about 1 cm in diameter, plain for the lower 2 cms or so and threaded above. A toothed wheel is secured tightly by two nuts at the lower end of the threaded portion. In my case this is a 72 tooth wheel taken from the unserviceable alarm clock. A third nut has 'shoulders' cut into its upper face and this moves freely up and down the rod. The pitch of my thread is about 67 turns to 1 cm but this figure is not important, providing you know what it is.

Arm A has a small part cut away from the outer end and the resulting projecting pieces pinched together slightly so that they rest on the shoulders cut in the nut.

The operating handle bears a small pawl (cut from scrap brass) which engages with the toothed wheel and below this a cam is arranged so that the arc of its engagement may be controlled. By adjusting the position of the cam the pawl can be made to engage after passing any number of teeth from a minimum of two to a maximum of about twenty. To avoid backlash I fixed a short piece of clock spring to bear on the toothed wheel and another, lighter piece of spring to hold the pawl in.

The threaded rod with wheel, cam and operating arm are concentric with the bush in the baseboard. Stops are fixed to the baseboard to limit the travel of both cam and operating handle.

OPERATION OF THE MECHANISM

This is dual:

1. When the handle is moved as far as it will go, the outer end of arm B is pulled down towards the baseboard by the cord against the tension of the springs. Releasing the handle allows the springs to pull the inner (specimen) end down to the resting position again. If knife and specimen are adjusted vis a vis each other a section will be cut.

   Since the specimen is moved in an arc the section will not be a truly straight cut but will be a small part of a large cylinder. The radius of the arc is about 10 cms and as the sections will be only a few millimetres across the curved effect is minimal and can be disregarded.

2. The operating handle also activates the advance mechanism. At a point in the travel of the handle, determined by the setting of the cam, the pawl engages with the toothed wheel and turns is slightly. The shoulderd nut on the rod cannot turn because it is held captive by the projecting pieces of Arm A. It therefore moves up the rod carrying arm A with it. This tilts the brass cage and moves the specimen chuck forward.

   For example, suppose the cam is set so that the pawl engages with every 12th tooth, the wheel is turned $\frac{12}{72}$ or $\frac{1}{6}$th of a full turn. The pitch of the threads on my rod is seven turns per centimetre or 1.42857 mm per turn. One sixth of this is .2381 mm. The relation between the length of arm A and the distance between the two pivots is 20 cms to 2 cms (or ten to one).

   This reduces the forward movement to .0238 mm or 24 microns. The two teeth would give an advance of $\frac{1}{6}$ of this or 4 microns and so on. This is a little too thin for normal practice and in any case it would be difficult to hone a knife sharp enough to cut so thinly. 8 to 10 microns is about

42

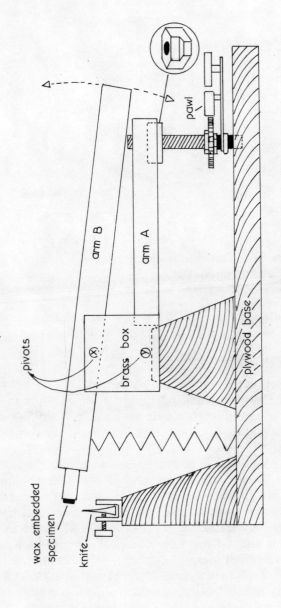

Fig. 18   The principle of the rocking microtome. Arm B swings on pivot X, moving the specimen across the blade of the knife. Arm A is integral with the brass box. If the righthand end of arm A is raised slightly the brass box moves on pivot Y and the specimen is advanced towards the knife.

47

Fig. 19 Details of microtome operating arm. The illustration shows the shoulders cut into the nut (the operating arm has been raised for clarity), and the cam and pawl mechanism.

right and can be achieved with the machine we are describing.

A HOT PLATE

There are many occasions when moderate heat is needed; for instance drying smears, melting glycerine jelly prior to mounting, keeping stained glycerine jelly mounts in a molten state for short periods to enable the stain to penetrate the mounted objects, etc.

The embedding oven described elsewhere is much too hot for these purposes. Gentler heat is needed. The laboratory apparatus for doing this is a thermostatically controlled and adjustable low temperature electric oven. I find that a satisfactory substitute is a large tin six or seven inches in diameter and about the same height, upended and with a hole cut in the top (which was the bottom) to take a small glass glycerine jelly container. Below the hole and inside the tin fix a shelf of sheet metal so that your jelly bottle rests on it inside the tin but with the neck and stopper above the level of the hot plate in a position where it is easily accessible. Heat is provided by a 40 watt bulb.

Fig. 20   The writer's home-made hot plate. Its battered appearance is a testament to its usefulness and longevity.

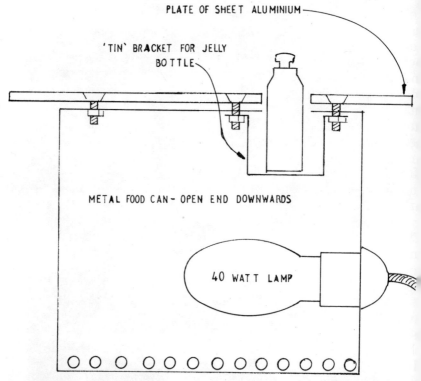

PLATE OF SHEET ALUMINIUM

'TIN' BRACKET FOR JELLY BOTTLE

METAL FOOD CAN - OPEN END DOWNWARDS

40 WATT LAMP

Fig 21   IMPROVISED HOT PLATE – diagramatic representation of Figure 20.

Fasten a sheet of fairly heavy gauge metal (say ⅛ in. thick about eight inches square over the top of the tin with small countersunk bolts. This will be your hot plate. I find this holds and dissipates heat very well and forms a stable platform on which to rest slides when needed.

During winter months when central heating is in operation the heat rising from a room radiator can be used. Make two wooden 'saddles' to sit over the top of the radiator and join them with a piece of stout wire mesh about ten inches by four. This will make a good drying rack for slides but will not usually be adequate for melting glycerine jelly.

A CENTRIFUGE

There is no doubt that a centrifuge is a very useful acquisition for the amateur microscopist. Ex Medical Corps field centrifuges

46

ome on the market from time to time and are worth buying. They usually need some kind of protective case but are otherwise serviceable for our purposes. I often wonder, too, what has become of the hand operated centrifuges which were so common in our grandfathers' days in laboratories and the consulting rooms of General Practitioners. If you come across a second-hand machine of any kind make sure that the tube buckets swing into a horizontal position when the machine is revolving. Some cheap centrifuges were made with the buckets fixed at an angle. These are an abomination. Sediment is deposited in a long streak down the tubes making it almost impossible to get a 100% collection and tube breakages are frequent unless you use plastic tubes. These are less easy to clean and sterilise than glass.

An adequate substitute for the proper article can be made up. The motive power is a domestic electric hand drill firmly gripped in the jaws of a carpenter's vice on a bench or on the now ubiquitous 'Workmate'. Speed can be controlled with a dimmer switch but check that its rating is man enough for the job in hand.

A mandrel for use with small grinding wheels – the kind available in multiple stores or DIY shops is suitable. The mandrel is screwed tightly to a short (4 in.) length of metal channel. I use sheet aluminium for this because because it is easily bent, cut, drilled and filed. Smaller U-pieces are pivoted in the ends of the channel by steel bolts. About 6 BA is right. Each U-piece is drilled and filed to take a metal bucket for the tubes. I made my buckets from short lengths of half inch copper water pipe. One end was stopped by soldering on a copper disc and the other end was gently hammered out to form a circular lip which would rest on the U-pieces.

The stem of the mandrel is held in the chuck of the drill. This stem should be quite short. They usually are but anything longer than say two inches should be cut down. A long stem introduces whip and as the speed of the drill increases the whole thing becomes uncontrollable.

A set up, such as has been just described, is very dangerous indeed. When the drill is revolving at speed it is absolutely essential to provide a cover to enclose it. This need be no more than a box of three ply or hardboard with strips of batten at the corners. Access to the tubes and buckets is via a hinged lid.

I like to screw my box down to the bench with two small angle pieces in an effort to reduce noise and vibration. This also

Fig. 22

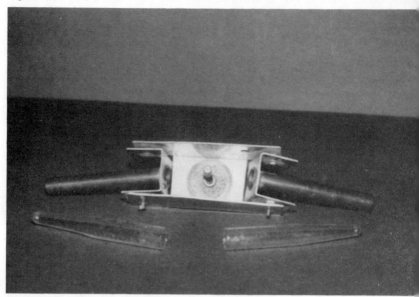

Fig. 22a. DIY head for centrifuge.

Fig. 22b. Centrifuge head in drill chuck and drill in bench vice. Note speed control.

48

Fig. 22c. Safety cover installed. This is IMPERATIVE.

prevents the box moving and the buckets coming into contact with the sides of the box. I fear that even so the noise level is high. The box seems to act like an amplifier.

I used an arrangement on these lines for some years until I found a second-hand centrifuge at my price and did useful work with it.

4. DISSECTING

DISSECTING

Vertebrates have a more or less rigid internal bony skeleton which supports and protects the internal organs and also provides anchorage points for the muscles. Bees have a hard external casing (the exoskeleton) to protect the viscera and prevent dessication. Most of the muscles are attached either to the exoskeleton or to projections from it internally. There are also internal struts, phragmae and tentoria, which add strength to the box-like exoskeleton.

The viscera float freely in the abdominal cavity, bathed in the haemolymph. There is no arterial system although there is a simple 'heart' which pumps the haemolymph in a circulatory system. The trachea and finely branched tracheoles are all pervading. They facilitate gas exchange at the points where this is most needed – the areas of greatest muscular exertion and also help to anchor and hold the viscera in place.

As a result of these differences and because of the small size of our subjects, the techniques of dissection have to be somewhat different to those of larger biological specimens. The body has to be supported firmly without injury to it and without distortion by contraction. Dissection must be under a fluid so that the soft internal parts are immediately supported when released.

I do not claim that the tools and methods described in the following sections are necessarily the only ones but I have found them reliable, practical, and above all, cheap.

The Tools of the Trade

These need be only quite simple but should be of good quality. The essentials are:

1. Prismatic erecting microscope giving a magnification of not more than 30 times.

2. Source of intense light.
3. Spirit lamp.
4. Piece of stout brass wire 6 in. long with about $\frac{3}{4}$ in. at one end bent at right angles.
5. Two needles with the 'eye' ends set firmly into pen holder-type handles. The needles should be fairly stiff. Fine sewing needles are too flexible.
6. Double needle for acarine dissection. This consists of two needles separated by the shaft of a stout pin. I find it satisfactory to bind the three portions together with fuse wire and then run a little epoxy resin adhesive over the binding.
7. Scalpel. I like the Swann Morton handles with a packet of No. 11 blades. When they become blunt they can be honed on a fine oilstone.
8. Pair of surgeons scissors. These *cannot* be improvised at home and it is worth while to buy the very best you can. The finest have narrow blades which cut right to the tip and have a very shallow profile. Here again the blades can be gently honed on an oilstone.
9. Pipette – fountain filler-type with rubber teat.
10. Fine and coarse forceps. For the fine, watchmakers' forceps No. 'S' are good.
11. One or two dissecting pans. These are small metal containers $2\frac{1}{2}$ in. to 3 in. in diameter filled to within $\frac{1}{4}$ in. of the top with beeswax. Empty shoe polish tins are good. So are typewriter ribbon containers although these are perhaps a little small for a man's hand. Use metal tins not plastic; you will need to apply heat from time to time.

These are all the tools you really need, but as time goes on and you get more proficient no doubt you will find yourself making other simple devices to meet your particular needs. For instance, I have found the following altered dissecting needles useful:

Heat the tip of a needle cherry red and turn over the very end into a tiny hook.

Heat another needle. Hammer the last $\frac{3}{8}$ in. flat and bend it at an angle of about 30°. Rub down both flat faces on fine emerycloth until this portion is as thin as possible. I find this useful as a lifter for small items, to pass under the viscera and such jobs as freeing the fine network of tracheoles.

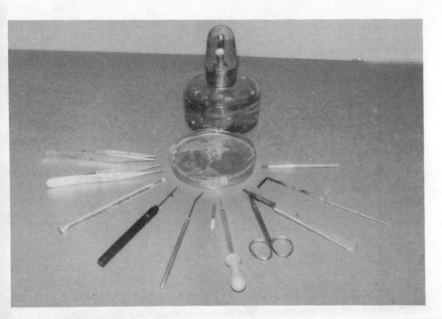

Fig. 23   Essential dissecting tools.

DISSECTING TECHNIQUE

Before starting on practical dissecting I think it is advisable to familiarise oneself with the main features of both the external and internal features of your subject. A list of suitable books is given under 'Further Reading', but here I must particularly recommend the late H. A. Dade's 'Anatomy and Dissection of the Honeybee'. This is altogether an admirable book and well worth having. All the plates are beautifully clear line drawings. Photographs of anatomical dissections are useless. They show too much detail in a jumbled way and a great deal of this detail serves no purpose other than to confuse the beginner. It could be said that Dade's line drawings are perhaps a little stylised but they are none the worse for that and all unnecessary details are omitted. The plates are arranged so that they may be folded out of the body of the book in order that they may be frequently referred to while the text is read.

I do not suggest for a moment that book knowledge is any substitute for practical experience, but it is a great aid to have in one's mind a general outline (and it need be no more than that) of the features likely to be found.

Probably your first two or three dissections will be less neat than you would have liked and some may even be disasters. Never mind. Press on and learn by your mistakes. In no time at all the needed manual dexterity will come.

Setting up the Bench

Arrange your workbench with your dissecting microscope in front of your chair. Focus the light source on the stage on which you have placed a dissecting pan. Tools and spirit lamp to the right and small bottle of 50% alcohol to the left (Industrial Methylated Spirit 50 parts by volume, cooled boiled water 45 parts by volume). The violet 'meths.' obtainable in hardware shops is no good. Dilution with water immediately produces a cloudy, not to say, opaque liquid.

KILLING

Never set to work on an animal or an insect unless it has been killed painlessly and with the muscles relaxed. The vapour of any volatile fluid (e.g. petrol) will kill but often the muscles will be contracted and the bees curled up. Chloroform is the best agent but may be difficult to come by. The next best is, I think, ethyl acetate and this is easily obtained at naturalist's shops. It is usually called 'Killing Fluid'. If there is any doubt about muscle relaxation these shops also sell a 'Relaxing Fluid' for use after killing.

Put two drops of your killing fluid on a small piece of filter or blotting paper and slip this inside the matchbox in which you will have secured your bees. In 30 seconds all the occupants will be dead. Do not be in too much of a hurry to tip them out on your bench. These chemicals are anaesthetics and if you are too quick the bees may recover in the fresh air and start to walk around – and eventually fly off.

Mounting the Specimen in the Dissecting Pan

Cut off the legs and wings with a small pair of scissors as close to the thorax as possible. If the bee has died with the proboscis extended, cut this off too. An old pair of scissors will do for this – not your best dissecting scissors.

Heat the bent end of your brass wire in the flame of the spirit lamp and with it melt a little pool of wax in the pan.

Fig. 24 Dissecting technique

Fig. 24a. Melting a pool of wax in the dissecting pan.

Fig 24b. Placing the insect in the pool of molten wax.

55

Fig. 24c. Making the first incision. Note the scissors steadied on the thumb of the left hand.

Hold the bee by the thorax, dorsal side uppermost, with the coarse forceps and lower it into the pool of wax. If you can contrive to lower the tip of the abdomen first and then the rest of the body, *gently* pulling it forward, the abdomen will be slightly extended by stretching the inter-segmental membranes. Reverse the brass rod and with the straight (cool) end hold the thorax down into the wax until it sets. The object is to embed the body in the wax to about half its depth.

Reheat the bent end of the wire and pull up a little more wax round the body walls.

Immediately flood with 50% alcohol. This does two things. It wets the bees body. If pure water is used many tiny air bubbles are trapped in the external hairs on the bees exoskeleton. The same thing happens inside the body when you get down to it. Secondly, the weak alcohol starts the process of fixation (q.v. under 'Methods with specific material and formulae'). You may decide to preserve some of your best dissections.

DISSECTION OF THE HEAD

Dade recommended that wax alone is too soft for head dissections and that a resin mix is to be preferred. However, dissections *can* be carried out in the usual wax dissecting pans providing the heads are embedded deeply in the wax and your scalpel is kept sharp.

Dissections from both anterior and posterior aspects should be made.

Anterior Aspect

Cut off the antennae.

With the scalpel cut round the edges of the compound eyes, not letting the point penetrate beyond the tip.

The head is strengthened by two internal chitinous posts (the tentoria). The external ends of these are marked by small pits just below the antennae in a groove which runs round the clypeus. Cut round these.

The front of the 'face' should now lift off exposing, in the case of young bees, the massive hypopharyngeal glands with their plump acini. The mandibular glands lie on either side of the clypeus.

Removal of the hypopharyngeal glands will disclose the brain and the great optic lobes. The radiating ommatidia can be seen if the compound eyes are cut down to the level of the optic lobes.

Posterior Aspect

Cut round the back of the head as was done for the anterior aspect. The tentoria lie on either side of the hole marking the articulation with the thorax (the foramen). They are also marked by pits. Free by cutting round them.

Lift off the back wall of the head.

The post cerebral glands are now to be seen and if these are lifted out the brain and the sub-oesophageal ganglion are clear to view.

DISSECTING THE THORAX

The thorax is completely filled with the indirect flight muscles lying in closely packed bundles nearly vertically and nearly horizontally. They form a gelatinous mass firmly attached to the roof, floor, anterior and posterior walls of the thoracic 'box'. In a freshly killed specimen it is difficult to remove them and impossible to do so neatly.

When bees have been immersed in a preserving fluid for a week or so the muscles lose their elasticity and become leathery.

In this condition it is easy to pluck them out in small bunches with forceps although, of course, they will still be attached to the thoracic walls. The answer is therefore always to use preserved bees for thoracic dissections.

Mount a preserved bee, minus legs and wings, in a dissecting pan as described in the section on dissecting the abdomen.

Using the tip of the scalpel and cutting outwards and forwards, cut a ring round the top of the thorax somewhat above the wing roots.

Make another cut fore and aft down a median line. The 'roof' will still not come off because of the muscle attachments.

Insert the scalpel horizontally through the ring you have cut and gradually cut through the muscles near the roof until one-half becomes free and can be lifted off with the forceps.

Repeat on the other half. This is a good test as to whether your scalpel blade is really sharp.

You are now left with the pinkish muscles exposed. Note their disposition.

If your intention is merely to get down to the nerve ganglia a rather crude alternative method sometimes works.

Cut the ring and the median line as before and then try to peel back the roof gently with the forceps. Some of the muscle bundles will be detached from the floor and will come up adhering to the roof: some will tear at the roof end and will remain in the thorax. Since your object is to get rid of the flight muscles the resulting untidiness does not matter too much. Those remaining can be removed as described below.

With the scissors enlarge the opening by cutting all round down to the wing roots.

Remove the muscles by grasping bundles of them with the forceps and pulling upwards. Do not push the forceps in too far while doing this so as not to damage the two furcae and the nerve ganglia below.

The furcae are chitinous strenthening bridges which lie transversely in the lower part of the thorax.

Anatomically there are really three furcae but the larger, posterior one, is in fact the fusion of two. Tiny pits on the outside of the ventral surface indicate the positions of attachment.

Under the first furca (working back from the head) lies a fairly large ganglion from which nerves run to the front legs. Under the second furca is a much larger ganglion. This controls the middle and back legs and the flight muscles. Smaller bundles of muscles can be seen at the bases of the wings. These control the pitch and angle of attack of the wings. They are sometimes called the direct flight muscles.

DISSECTION OF THE ABDOMEN

Your specimen is now firmly embedded in wax and covered with weak alcohol.

Hold the pan by encircling it with the forefinger and thumb of the left hand (lefthanders reverse). The head of the bee should be pointing away from you and a little to the left.

Holding the scissors in the right hand rest them on the rim of the pan so that they are up against your left thumb, which from now on will be a guide.

Insert the tip of the inside blade in the intersegmental membrane behind the rearmost visible segment.

With small snips cut through the body wall moving forwards. Try to keep the scissors with the inside blade nearly parallel with the body wall.

As the direction of the cut changes, for example when you get to the thorax, do not move your scissor hand outward to compensate, but turn the pan to the right so that the scissors are always resting against your left thumb.

Continue right round the abdomen until you reach the point of your first insertion.

You should now be able to lift off the dorsal side of the abdomen like a roof and expose the viscera. The dorsal diaphragm and the heart will come away with the 'roof.'

You will quite likely find that the roof is tied to the viscera by a fine network of tracheoles. These show up as silvery threads. Break them with the needles to free the roof.

5. SOME BASIC PROCESSES IN THE PREPARATION OF MATERIALS

FIXATION

At the moment of death any organism, the cells of which it is made, immediately start to decompose. This is caused by two processes. Autolysis, the natural breaking down of the internal material of the cells once the life principle ceases and by attack by the ever present bacteria which feed on organic material. Complete decomposition of the organism ensues unless some preservative action is taken.

Our object in making microscopical preparations is to arrest the decomposition and to preserve the material in as lifelike a condition as possible and to harden the tissues so that they will withstand handling and further treatment. This is what the microscopist means by fixation. After fixation the material is ready to be stained and preserved.

There is a widely held belief that alcohol is the best fixative and preservative. I do not think this is the case. Alcohol does not penetrate quickly enough and prolonged immersion in it makes the tissues leathery. There is no single substance which will fix cell and tissue components with complete satisfaction. All fixatives have their advantages and disadvantages. The best plan is to use a mixture of two or more fluids so that the advantages of one will offset the disadvantages of the other. Certainly, to start with, it is a good idea to familiarise oneself with one of the more common mixtures until further experiment is suggested by advancing expertise. The specialist in cytological and histological research will have his own favourites.

Since rapid penetration of the fixative is needed, tissue should be cut into pieces no larger than say 1 cm by $\frac{1}{2}$ cm if they are taken from a larger mass. Most insect parts will be so small that no further sub-division will be needed. Use plenty of fixative – by volume 100 parts of fixative to 1 part of tissue is not too much.

Of the many fixatives available the following is a short-list of those which are useful, can be made up easily, and are readily obtainable ready made up from naturalists' sundriesmen:–

Characteristics of Fixatives

Fixative	Penetration and time needed for fixation	Wash in	Shrinkage	Hardening
Acetic Acid. Good for nuclei and Chromosomes.	Very rapid. About 1 hour – not longer.	Alcohol (70%)	Swells tissues very much.	None
Alcohol (Ethyl). Not satisfactory at low temperatures. Does not fix chromatin.	Fair. 1 to 3 hours.	Alcohol	Shrinks very much.	Fairly great.
Bouin's Fluid. Good for chromosomes.	Fair. 12 to 18 hours.	Alcohol (70%)	Little	Little
Carnoy's Fluid. Good for nuclei & cytoplasm. Not good for plant tissue.	Rapid. Half an hour.	Alcohol (100%)	Slight	None
Formaldehyde. Makes outline of nuclei less clear.	Slow. 1 to 2 days.	Alcohol (70%)	Considerable	Great
Formalin-Alcohol. A good general fixative.	Rapid. 15 minutes.	Alcohol (70%)	Characteristics are a combination of those of the three constituents.	
Formol-Acetic-Alcohol.	Rapid. 15 minutes.	Alcohol (70%)		

Please also see under 'Formulae'.

Of the above short list I have found Bouin's and Formol-Acetic-Alcohol the most satisfactory.

STAINING

After fixation, in an unstained tissue the only parts distinguishable from one another are those having different refractive indices. Under phase-contrast microscopy these differences in refractive index are converted into differences in light intensity so that small striae, perforations, etc., will become clearly visible where, without phase-contrast they would be indiscernible.

Phase-contrast is beyond the reach of most amateur microscopists and is mentioned for interest only. Some other method of distinguishing detail must be used. Staining is the answer. Staining with different dyes or with different intensities of the same dye will render the different components of a piece of tissue well defined.

Stains may be classified as:–
1. Histological – i.e. they define and differentiate tissues.
2. Cytological – i.e. they define cell components.
   Cytological stains may be further divided into:
      (a) Cytoplasmic – they have an affinity for the cell cytoplasm.
      (b) Nuclear – thay have an affinity for the cell nucleus.

An example of a nuclear stain in figure 27. In an effort to show the mitotic dividing of chromosomes I slightly overstained my section with chlorazol black and then differentiated with dilute Milton until the stain was removed from the cell contents other than the nuclei and chromosomes.

Many stains can be used. A selection is given under 'Formulae'. However, again in the interests of simplicity, I think it best to confine oneself to perhaps two stains until familiarity with their characteristics becomes second nature.

DIFFERENTIATION

This is just a rather grand name for destaining. The purpose is to remove excess stain so that contrast between stained parts and those less stained is greatest.

The three major differentiation agents are:–
   Clove oil – good with Crystal Violet stain.
   Acid Alcohol (70% Alcohol with the addition of 0.5% Hydrochloric Acid.)
   Milton – good with Chlorazol black.

The process is often rapid especially in the case of Acid Alcohol. Careful observation under the low power of a microscope is advisable. After differentiation wash in 70% Alcohol.

DEHYDRATION

Water will not mix with the resinous material in which specimens are finally mounted nor with paraffin wax (if sectioning is contemplated).

The commonest dehydrating agent in use in the past was ethyl alcohol. Unfortunately it is liable to distort tissues unless used in a number of graded strengths and it is expensive and as it is very hygroscopic it is almost impossible to be maintained at 100% pure. The cheaper iso-propyl alcohol or acetone may be used in the final stages.

A much better dehydrating agent is ethylene glycol mono-ethyl ether – sold as 'Cellosolve'. It is readily obtainable without Excise permit. It is miscible with water and xylene, which is, itself miscible with paraffin wax.

Methods in Use.

Using Cellosolve.

Does not distort thin pieces of tissue but should not be used for large pieces.

There is no need to grade the dehydration. Material may be transported from water into pure Cellosolve and also into Cellosolve from any strength of alcohol.

Dehydration is complete in about one minute.

It is miscible with clove oil.

Using Ethyl Alcohol.

When most tissues are transferred from water to 100% alcohol the water is removed too rapidly. As a result they are subject to shrinkage and distortion. Gradual dehydration in alcohol of graded strengths is needed. For instance:–

	Bulk Tissue	*Sections*
1. Alcohol 30%	30 mins	1 min
2. Alcohol 50%	30 mins	1 min
3. Alcohol 70%	30 mins	1 min
Then either		
4. Alcohol 90%	6 hours	2 mins
5. Alcohol 90% (fresh)	6 hours	2 mins
6. Alcohol 100%	6 hours	2 mins
7. Alcohol 100% (fresh)	6 hours	2 mins
or:–		
4. Industrial meths	6 hours	2 mins
5. Industrial meths (fresh) ...	6 hours	2 mins
6. Isopropyl alcohol or acetone	6 hours	2 mins
7. Isopropyl alcohol or acetone (fresh)	6 hours	2 mins

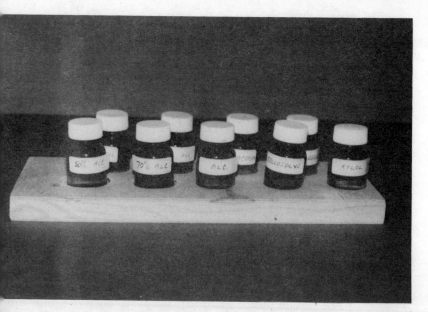

A rack of small bottles for reagents is both useful and economical.

It is economical to use small containers for the various liquids ı which we need to soak our specimens. The small bottles used y chemists for pills are ideal. Use glass bottles – not the modern lastic variety. These are dissolved by some solvents!

If small 'ladles' are made from perforated zinc with wire andles these can be lifted out with the specimen in situ and :ansferred to the next reagent. Remember that you will be radually diluting the grades of dehydrating agent, etc., so the nal bottle will have to be renewed from time to time.

It seems a little tiresome to have so many steps to go through ut dehydration *must* be complete. Incomplete dehydration will esult in a whitish film when you get to the xylene stage and the pecimen will be quite spoiled.

:LEARING

Alcohol is not miscible either with paraffin wax or the esinous media used for making permanent mounts. These esinous substances are usually dissolved in xylene or some milar hydro-carbon derivative.

The object of clearing is to remove the alcohol (or Cellosolve) and to replace it with a more compatible solvent. When a specimen is thoroughly soaked with the clearing agent its refractive index is raised and it becomes more transparent.

Xylene is, or was, often used as a clearing agent but it tends to shrink and harden tissues and, as already noted, incomplete dehydration will result in a milky film (probably the result of emulsification).

Cedar oil is the best for fine work with animal tissue.

There are two qualities available – for clearing and for use with oil immersion objectives. The former is cheaper. Drops of the oil tend to remain in the specimen. A quick rinse in xylene just prior to mounting will put this right. Prepared specimens may be left in cedar oil indefinitely.

For fine work with plant material use clove oil. I think it works just as well as cedar oil but has the drawback that it will remove a number of stains after prolonged immersion, e.g. haematoxylin, crystal violet, orange G and Safranin O. If any of these stains have been used in your processing make a quick rinse in cedar oil and then another in xylene.

WAX EMBEDDING.

Animal tissues are not usually sufficiently rigid and before sectioning it is necessary for the specimen to be impregnated with, and then embedded in, a suitable supporting material. The usual substance for this is paraffin wax with a melting point of 48°C to 53°C – not higher. The specimen may be stained in bulk before sectioning or stained after the sections have been cut and secured on to micro slides. The latter is by far the best.

The fixed, dehydrated and cleared tissue is gradually brought through increasing strengths of paraffin wax in a solvent until they are sitting in pure molten wax (two baths). Impregnation is easier if the specimens are first steeped in half strength wax.

Excessive heat must be avoided and the molten wax or wax mixture should only be fractionally hotter than its melting point. If some kind of embedding oven such as is described elsewhere in this book with top heat is used it can be adjusted so that the heat from above is no more than enough to melt the top half of the wax in its container. The specimen will then rest at the junction between the molten and the solid wax – that is at the point where the wax is just melting.

Use small containers such as the ubiquitous domestic paste pots which only hold a couple of ounces or so. After use do not throw the wax away. It improves with use and after about a year of repeated heating and cooling it seems to set with a smoother texture. The addition of a very small amount of ceresin seems to help in this regard too.

After impregnation the specimen is embedded in a block of wax of a size suitable for attachment to the chuck of the microtome.

Two methods of making a mould are:–

(a) Cut two pieces from brass sheet about $\frac{1}{16}$ in. thick, each $\frac{1}{2}$ in. by $1\frac{5}{8}$ in. Bend each to an L shape with sides 1 in. and $\frac{5}{8}$ in. Stand the L pieces on a sheet of glass to form a box.

(b) Make a box of stiff paper (good quality note paper is about right) from a sheet $1\frac{5}{8}$ in by 3 in. Fold as directed by the note at the foot of the illustration. (Figure 26).

There is another method of impregnation sometimes used in laboratories and that is the use of celloidin (purified nitro cellulose) and freezing into a gel. I do not think this method holds any advantages for the beginner and will not be described here.

EMBEDDING

The wax impregnated specimen is now ready for the mould. Pour molten wax into your mould, either the brass L pieces or the paper mould according to your choice.

Warm your forceps or a section lifter and quickly place the specimen in the molten wax.

Orientate the specimen as desired with warm needles.

Quickly fill the mould with more molten wax. It may be necessary to hold the specimen in position with warm needles.

Cool the wax rapidly in order to minimise crystallisation. Hold the mould on the surface of a bowl of cold water and blow gently on the surface of the wax. As soon as a skin forms on the surface of the wax tilt the mould slightly and immerse it in the cold water. If you have used paper moulds it is well to make a note of the specimen and the direction in which it is lying if it is longitudinal. This can be done on the projecting flaps of the mould. If you are using brass L pieces make your notes on a slip of paper and insert it in the end of the mould before the wax solidifies.

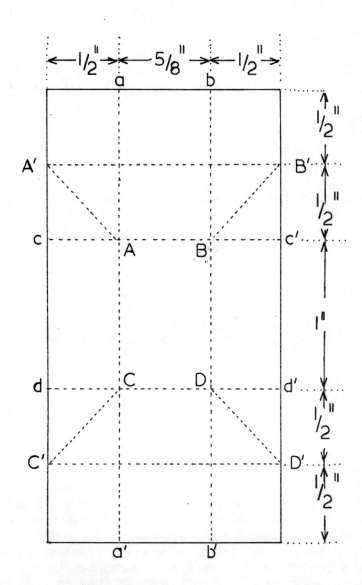

Fig. 26 A paper mould for wax embedding.
Make all folds inwards.
Fold a a' and b b'
Fold c c' and d d'
Fold A' A, B' B, C' C, and D' D.
Turn the 'dog's ears' round against the ends of the box. Turn down, outside, th
projecting flaps remaining. These can be used for noting contents.

ECTIONING

Remove the wax block from its mould and pare away the wax ɔ that practically none remains at the sides of the specimen and ery little at the top and bottom. Ensure that the upper and lower ɪrfaces of the block are parallel. Cut off a tiny portion of the lock on its front face (i.e. the face which will meet the knife first).

Melt the old wax on the chuck of the microtome with the eated blade of an old scalpel – or perhaps the handle of your ɔod scalpel.

Press the wax block firmly on to the warmed chuck so that it ill be be parallel with the knife blade.

Cool under the tap.

Fix the chuck on the microtome and proceed to cut your ɛctions – not too thin at first. Try 8 to 12 microns. If you are lucky ɪd if you have carried out all the steps correctly the sections ɪould come off in a ribbon. Support this on the forefinger of the ɛe hand. If the sections come off the knife separately lift them f with a small camel hair brush.

Throw the sections on the surface of a bowl of hot water – ɔout as hot as the hand will stand comfortably. The hot water ill remove all the wrinkles in the sections and flatten them. Take ɾe here. If the water is too hot the wax may liquify and the sec- ɔns will be lost.

If the sections do not come off in a ribbon:–

(a) The wax may be too hard. Warm it gently. I have repeatedly found this problem in the winter. The answer is to work in a warm room and to see that the microtome, knife and wax blocks have been in the warm for some time.

(b) The knife may be too cold. See under (a).

(c) The knife may be greasy. Wipe it with xylene.

(d) The upper and lower surfaces of the wax block may not be parallel. Correct.

(e) The xylene may not have been completely removed before the final impregnation. Return to pure wax for further impregnation.

If the sections and the specimen tears:–

(a) The razor may be blunt – resharpen.

(b) The specimen may not have been properly fixed.

(c) The fixative may not have been completely washed out.

(d) Dehydration and impregnation may have been imper
fectly carried out.

Attachment of Sections to Slides

The adhesive used for the attachment of sections to micr
slides must be strong enough to hold the section to the slid
during subsequent manipulations but at the same time it must n
interfere with these manipulations. The substance common
used is egg albumen with glycerine although human saliva ofte
works quite well. The adhesive can be bought ready made and
well worth the few pence it costs. There are few things so co
ducive to bad language as seeing a fine section which has take
ten days to produce, gently float off the slide when you try
dissolve off the wax. The bottle I have in current use was boug
some twenty years ago and is still half full.

Make your slide grease free by a thorough wash in water plu
household detergent. Rinse off under the tap.

Smear the slide very sparingly with adhesive. The edge of th
hand drawn from end to end of the slide produces an even smear

Pass the slide under the section and let it be drawn on by su
face tension.

Remove excess water by gently covering with filter paper.

Dry overnight in a warm situation. The airing cupboard or
shelf above a central heating radiator will do the job but provi
some cover for your slide. The great enemy at this stage is dust.

Wax removal and staining

The following processes may be carried out by pouring t
reagents gently on to the slide and draining off after the appr
priate time but it is probably better to immerse the whole slide
the reagent. Special glass containers known as 'staining jars' c
be bought for this but I have found that the upright glass co
tainers of various culinary herbs on sale at all stores and groc
are equally good for a few slides. The herb jars will comfortab
hold two slides back to back and need be filled only a little ov
half way with the reagents.

Warm the slide very gently until the *edges* of the wax ju
begin to melt.

Immediately plunge into xylene. The wax will dissolve in t
xylene and the time taken for this will vary according to the thic
ness of the wax. Allow half an hour to be safe.

70

The section is now ready for staining. Immerse in alcohol (1 minute) and then hydrate if necessary down to the strength of the stain used. For instance if you are using Borax-Carmine, this is 50% alcohol/water so plunge your slide in 50% alcohol for one minute before staining. If you are using, say, Crystal Violet, as this is an alcoholic stain transfer directly into the stain from the alcohol bath.

Then differentiate, wash in alcohol and clear in cedar oil.

A quick rinse in xylene.

Place a *small* drop of Canada Balsam in xylene on the section and lower a cover glass with forceps.

Label the slide and put it in a safe place to dry off for 24 hours.

The production of a good, even a passable section is not difficult but it is tedious and each stage requires care.

Suggested specimen schedule for sectioning for example the ventriculus of a honeybee.

1. Kill insect. Chloroform or Ethyl Acetate (Entomologist's 'Killing Fluid').
2. Immediately and quickly dissect out ventriculus under 50% alcohol.
3. Dehydrate in Cellosolve. 30 minutes. No gradation of strengths needed.
4. Fresh Cellosolve 10 minutes.
5. Clove oil (Clearing grade) 24 hours.
6. 50/50 cedar oil/paraffin wax 1 hour.
7. Molten paraffin wax 1 hour.
8. Fresh molten paraffin wax 1 hour.
9. Embed in mould.
10. Cut sections.
11. Float sections on warm water.
12. Smear micro slide with adherent.
13. Pass slide under the section and draw it on with the aid of surface tension.
14. Remove excess water with filter paper.
15. Dry overnight in gentle warmth.
16. Warm slide gently until edges of wax begin the melt.
17. Immerse in xylene. $\frac{1}{2}$ hour.
18. Alcohol or Cellosolve at least one minute. Longer would be an advantage.
19. 50% alcohol 1 minute.

20. Borax-Carmine 2 minutes.
21. Differentiate in acid alcohol. Watch process under low power microscope.
22. Rinse in 50% alcohol (two changes).
23. Cellosolve 1 minute.
24. Xylene 1 minute.
25. Cedar oil 1 minute.
26. Quick rinse in xylene.
27. Mount in Canada Balsam in xylene.
28. Label slide.
29. Leave in dust free atmosphere to dry. 24 hours or more.

g. 27   Some examples of
ctions produced with
nple, home-constructed
icrotome.

ght.
dial section through
mpound eye of drone.

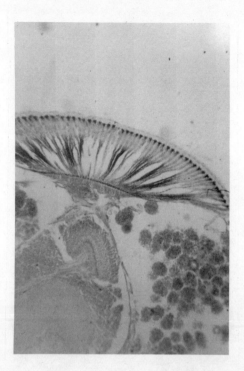

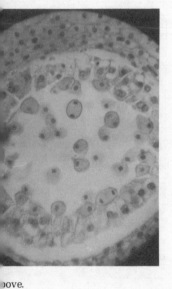

ove.
eiosis in lily anther.

ght.
owing tip of allium root
show chromosomes at
tosis.

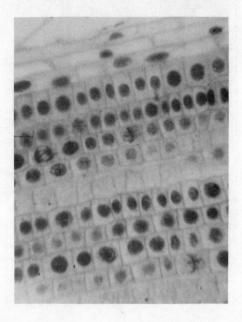

6. FORMULAE AND HINTS

FORMULAE AND HINTS

have included in this section formulae of some of the more popular stains and reagents, not because the ordinary reader will want to make them up himself, but so that he may know their alcoholic strengths. This is important for determining the pre- and post-staining baths.

It is probably cheaper in the long run to buy stains ready-made and this applies to some of the other media too, with the notable exception of glycerine jelly. The quality of the home-made variety of glycerine jelly is far superior to that of the bought kind in my experience. I have never discovered why this is, but it seems to be a fact nevertheless.

ACID ALCOHOL

Alcohol (industrial methylated spirit) 70% ....   100 c.c.
Hydrochloric acid ....   0.5 c.c.
A useful differentiating agent.

ALCOHOL

Absolute alcohol is normally unobtainable by the amateur. Even if it were it would not remain absolute for very long. If the stopper is left off the bottle or if anyone breathes across the open mouth, the alcohol is so very hygroscopic that dilution will occur. The dilution will, of course, be slight, but you might as well be content with Industrial Methylated Spirit which is 95% pure and quite good enough for our purposes. A Permit is needed and there is usually no difficulty in obtaining one from the local Customs and Excise Office. Having got your Permit under Methylated Spirit Regulations 1983 S.I. 1983/252, an application to a supplier must be made in writing in a form of wording which the Customs Officer will specify. The application must be signed and bear your reference number. The Permit will be valid for one year and wil be for a specified amount of alcohol.

BASIC FUCHSIN (sometimes called Aniline Red, Magenta o Rosaniline)

This is a very intense dye. Only the smallest quantity need b bought. Indeed, if you can find a few friends to share, this is eve better.

Dissolve a couple of crystals in 1 c.c. of Alcohol and add 16 c.c. of Distilled Water. Use this as your stock solution.

BORAX CARMINE (Grenacher's Alcoholic)

Borax .... 4 gr.
Distilled water .... 100 c.c.
Carmine .... 3 gr.
Heat the above then add:
Alcohol (70%) .... 100 c.c.
Allow to stand for two days then filter.

A good general and nuclear stain. Will stain the nucleus firs and then the cell cytoplasm. This is called 'progressive staining.'

BOUIN'S FLUID

Picric acid (saturated solution in water) .... 75 c.c.
Glacial acetic acid .... 5 c.c.
Formaldehyde (40%) .... 25 c.c.
A useful fixative for delicate tissues. Do not wash in wate Use 50% then 70% alcohol.

CANADA BALSAM

Dissolved in Xylene this is (or was) the traditional mountant fc dehydrated and cleared specimens. It still *can* be got but i expensive. It should be kept in the dark because it darkens i bright light and mounts will also do so after the passage of years.

There are a number of modern substitutes on the marke Two I have used are Practamount and Numount, trade names c the suppliers. Practamount is water clear and Numount is a pal straw colour – about the same as good Canada Balsam in Xylene. thought that the first named tended to shrink a little, especially i a thickish mount. Apart from this, both behaved satisfactorily bt remain to undergo the test of time.

CEDAR WOOD OIL
Two qualities are available, for clearing and for oil immersion objectives. When buying state which you want. The former is cheaper.

CHLORAZOL BLACK (Azo Black)
Chlorazol Black E (Biological quality) – as much as will dissolve in:

    Alcohol (70%) .... 100 c.c.

    Useful for bulk and section staining. Differentiate with dilute Milton.

CRYSTAL VIOLET (Gentian Violet)
Good stain for the nuclei of cells. Differentiate with Clove Oil.

TABLE FOR DILUTION OF LIQUIDS

Percentage strength of original liquid

Percentage strength of liquid required and volumes of original liquid to be taken	100	96	95	90	85	80	75	70	60	50	40	30	20
95	5	1											
90	10	6	5										
85	15	11	10	5									
80	20	16	15	10	5								
75	25	21	20	15	10	5							
70	30	26	25	20	15	10	5						
60	40	36	35	30	25	20	15	10					
50	50	46	45	40	35	30	25	20	10				
40	60	56	55	50	45	40	35	30	20	10			
30	70	66	65	60	55	50	45	40	30	20	10		
20	80	76	75	70	65	60	55	50	40	30	20	10	
15	85	81	80	75	70	65	60	55	45	35	25	15	5

Volumes of dilutent to be added

FORMALIN-ALCOHOL fixative
    Alcohol (70%) .... 100 c.c.
    Formaldehyde (40%) .... 6 c.c.

FORMO-ACETIC-ALCOHOL fixative
    Formaldehyde (40%) .... 5 c.c.
    Acetic acid (glacial) .... 7 c.c.
    Alcohol (70%) .... 90 c.c.

GLYCERINE JELLY

    Gelatine (Davis's culinary) .... 1 part by weight
    Distilled water .... 6 parts by weight
    Leave to soak for two hours then add:
    Glycerine .... 7 parts by weight
    Warm and stir until all the gelantine is dissolved (about 15 minutes).

For every 100 gr. of jelly add two crystals of pure thymol. Stir until the thymol is dissolved. The object of the thymol is to inhibit fungal growth. Too much will result in a milky appearance caused by undissolved flakes of thymol. Professionally produced, glycerine jelly is usually treated with phenol instead of thymol. I prefer thymol because phenol tends to cause fading of some stains.

I find that glycerine jelly is an excellent mountant for delicate tissues and its low refractive index enhances visibility.

If tissues have been treated with an alcoholic stain they should be brought down to water and then immersed in 50% glycerine for a few minutes before mounting. Those in aqueous stains can go straight into 50% glycerine.

KILLING

Insects (and other small animals) intended for dissection should be killed quickly and humanely and, if possible, with the muscles relaxed. There are a number of chemicals which will do this.

(a) Potassium cyanide. This is highly poisonous and moreover kills with the muscles contracted. It is NOT recommended.

(b) Almost any volatile oil. Petrol, benzene, xylene, chloroform, and ethyl acetate will all do the job.

(c) Cut up leaves of cherry laurel (prunus laurocerasus).

Of these Ethyl Acetate is the best. It is the basis of what naturalist's suppliers sell as 'Killing Fluid'. It has the great advantage that it kills with the muscles relaxed.

Apart from killing, the vapour from finely cut strips of cherry laurel is a good relaxant. Pack the strips in a wide-mouthed jar fairly tightly until about three-quarters full. Cut a piece of filter paper to fit the jar and press it down on the leaves. Keep the lid on and only release it to pop in any insects for killing or relaxing.

When killing with Ethyl Acetate, get the insects into an otherwise empty match box and slip in a small piece of filter (or blotting) paper on which you have sprinkled a few drops of the killing fluid. Chloroform is treated in the same way.

LACTO-PHENOL

A mountant which fixes and preserves at the same time.

Lactic acid (concentrated)	10 gr.
Phenol (crystals)	10 gr.
Glycerine	20 gr.

Permanent slides must be ringed. I have always found it difficult to make a really satisfactory ringing of liquid mounts. On the whole, the best ringing material is colourless nail varnish. The trick is to use only enough Lacto-phenol to reach nearly, but not quite, to the edge of the cover slip so that no cleaning up is necessary.

Lacto-phenol does two processes in the same operation. It fixes and makes a permanent mount at the same time.

METHYL BLUE

Methyl blue	1 gr.
Distilled water	99 c.c.

This is a good counterstain for carmine.

MILTON

Milton is a sterilising fluid sold for sterilising babies' feeding bottles, teats, etc. It is also an excellent differentiating agent, when diluted, after staining with Azo Black. It is hardly worthwhile making it up oneself as it is so cheap and easy to obtain. Its composition is:

Sodium hypochlorite	1.00%
Sodium chloride	16.50%
Sodium chlorate	0.13%
Sodium carbonate	0.05%
Sodium sulphate	0.15%
Calcium chloride	0.07%
Magnesium chloride	Trace
Water	82.10%

NEGATIVE STAIN

A stain which stains the background but not the specimen.

This is usually put up as an aqueous solution of nigrosin. I get better results with indian ink and, of these, 'Pelikan' brand is the best.

RAZOR SHARPENING

Time spent on honing the razor for the microtome is never wasted.

Use a fine stone and cover it with olive oil.

Sit at a table with the length of the stone parallel with the edge of the table and in front of you.

Place the razor blade quite flat on the stone at the lefthand edge with the heel rather in advance of the toe.

With gentle pressure pull the razor to the right edge first.

At the end of the stroke turn the razor over *on its back* and draw it back to the left edge first and with the heel a little advanced.

Continue this left to right and right to left movement, gradually decreasing the pressure until you are just 'stroking' the stone.

Before and after use always give the razor a good stropping.

REFRACTIVE INDICES

Air	1.000
Alcohol, methyl	1.323
Benzene	1.504
Canada balsam in xylene	1.524
Cedar wood oil	1.510
Clove oil	1.533
Glass (crown)	1.518
Glycerine (100%)	1.470
Glycerine (50%)	1.397
Lacto-phenol	1.440
Turpentine	1.470
Water (distilled)	1.336
Xylene	1.497

Using media with refractive indices lower than that of Canada balsam enhances visibility.

RINGING SLIDES

Slides of liquid or aqueous media need a ring of varnish at the edges of the cover slip to make a good joint with the slide.

Specimens mounted in Canada balsam in xylene require no ringing. Mounts in glycerine jelly and liquid mounting media do.

Gold size, Canada balsam in xylene, nail varnish and the special ringing cements sold under trade names are all good. Of these, I prefer nail varnish. The little bottles have an advantage in that each has its own little brush stuck in the cap.

SAFRANIN O (Cotton Red, Gossypimine)

Safranin O .... 1 gr.
Alcohol (50%) .... 99 c.c.
Do not use in glycerine jelly mounts.
This is another good stain for cell nuclei.

7. METHODS FOR SPECIFIC MATERIAL

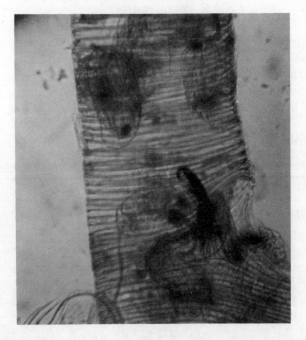

Fig. 28   Acarine dissection. The appearance of the main trachea when infested with mites.

AMERICAN FOUL BROOD (Bacillus Larvae)

From an infected comb extract a scale or a little slime in the brown 'ropy' stage. Rub this up in a drop of water on a microslide with a matchstick.

Place a drop of negative stain in the centre of another (grease-free) slide.

Sterilise a wire loop in a flame and take up a loopful of the suspension and transfer it to the negative stain. Stir well.

Make a thin smear on the slide by drawing across it with the edge of another slide.

Dry for a few minutes on your hot plate.

When thoroughly dry add a small drop of Canada Balsam in Xylene and add a cover slip.

The spores act as though they are slightly greasy; in any event they do not take the stain but appear as slender white cylinders with rounded ends when viewed via an oil immersion lens (1.3 by 0.5 microns).

In cases of American Foul Brood practically pure cultures of spores of Bacillus Larvae will be found.

The dead larvea will have contained a great deal of fat and this will appear as blank areas in your smear.

Grease-free slides are needed for any kind of smear. They are easy to prepare. Rub a few microslides between finger and thumb with a drop of neat domestic detergent (unscented!) on each side. Rinse off under the tap and allow to dry. Hold by the edges only.

Please remember that you are dealing with very virulent and infective spores. All apparatus used should be sterilised after use. Burn the match you have used and scrub the hands thoroughly. A final rinse with domestic bleach or sterilising fluid would not be too fussy.

AGARINE MITES

Dissect out the main tracheae from the first thoracic spiracles of an infected (or suspected infected) worker bee. The spiral strengthening of the tracheae and the carapace of the mites are chitinised and no staining is needed. Soak in 50% and then pure glycerine for half an hour each and then add to a drop of melted clear glycerine jelly on a slide. Cover with a cover slip. Leave overnight and then wash off any exuding jelly. Ring with nail varnish. The colour is immaterial but I think clear looks neater.

The mites will be clearly visible inside the lumen of the tracheae and (if you are lucky) one or two may escape into the surrounding jelly.

AMOEBA SPORES (Malpighamoeba Mellificae)

(1) Snip of the tip of the abdomen of a freshly killed bee.

Insert the fine forceps and withdraw the viscera. Usually the mid gut and hind gut come away with part of the rectum not cut off.

Place the viscera in a watch glass with a few drops of water. There will be a great deal of pollen and faeces.

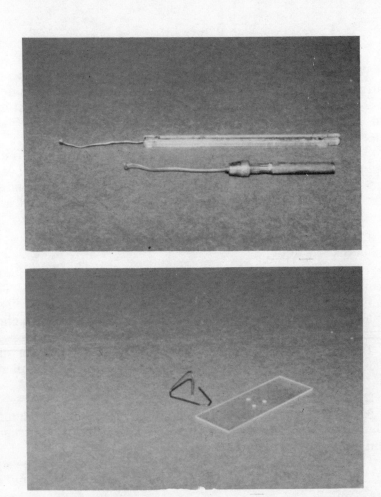

Fig. 29   Wire loops (top illustration). Above, 'professional' platinum wire loop in glass rod. Below, frame wire loop held in small chuck.

Aids to mounting (bottom illustration). Wire clip made from twisted paper clip and microslide with three paper wads for thick mounts.

Cut off a few malpighian tubules and transfer to a fresh watch glass on to a microslide. Change to fresh water in order to get rid of the floating pollen grains, etc.

In amoeba infection not all individuals will show cysts and it may be necessary to examine a number of individual bees until a good example is obtained.

Having found two or three tubules showing cysts soak them in 50% glycerine and then in pure glycerine (half-an-hour in each).

Place a drop of clear melted glycerine jelly on a clean micro-slide, put the tubules in the jelly and arrange with needles.

Warm a cover slip by passing through a flame and lower it gently on to the pool of jelly. Lower so that the edge of one side of the cover slip comes into contact with the pool of jelly first and then complete lowering. You may need to steady the cover slip with a needle while you are doing this.

Set aside in a cool place for 24 hours to set, then clean off any surplus jelly with cold water and a small camel hair brush. Leave to get quite dry and then apply a ring of nail varnish to the edges of the cover slip, making sure that the varnish makes contact with both slide and cover slip.

(2) Mass Technique

Snip off the complete abdomens of about 30 bees and drop into a mortar. Add a few drops of water and grind with the pestle. The small white pots used to pack 'Princess' paté make excellent mortars (you do not want anything too big). For a pestle use a glass 'swizzle' stick or even a short length of glass rod.

Tilt the mortar to one side and allow the dirty looking suspension to collect. Place two drops of this on a grease-free micro-slide.

Dry on the hot plate and mount in glycerine jelly.

Amoeba cysts are circular, or nearly so, about 7 to 8 microns in diameter. They are very refractive and present a hard black outline and are best viewed under a X40 objective.

Thrown slightly out of focus the contents of the cysts seem to be granular, but this may merely be an optical effect at the out of focus position.

(3) Smear in Negative Stain

Make a smear with a drop of the suspension. Dry on the hot plate and mount in glycerine jelly.

(4) Temporary Mounts

Place a drop of the suspension on a clean slide, add a cover slip and examine under a X40 objective.

This is a very quick and useful method of making routine examinations of suspected bees. It is worthwhile to familiarise yourself with the appearance of such temporary smears. There will be a great deal of debris of course, but with very little experience you will be able to spot any pathogens, especially Amoeba and Nosema (q.v.) spores.

ANTENNAE

Cut off an antenna from a freshly killed drone as close to the 'face' as possible.

Partially bleach to a light brown colour. The bleaching agent is chlorine. One way to get nascent chlorine is to put a few crystals of chlorate of potash into a pyrex test tube, add two drops of spirits of salts (concentrated hydrochloric acid) and then about a teaspoonful of water. Place the antenna in the tube and warm gently. Do not overheat.

However, this mixture of hot acid and potash is potentially dangerous and, although it is the normal laboratory method, a much safer way is to use dilute domestic bleach. The process should be watched to guard against overbleaching. This method equally applies to any chitinous parts.

I have sometimes found that bleaching occurs unevenly, giving a blotchy appearance. I fancy that this may be due to the thin oily/wax which covers the whole of the exoskeleton. A quick preliminary rinse in a solvent will clean off the oil. I have found acetone satisfactory.

After bleaching wash thoroughly in water (several changes).

Transfer the antenna to a 10% solution of caustic potash.

Leave for up to two days. This will dissolve out the soft internal parts. After this maceration wash in water – six changes with half-an-hour in each.

Dehydrate in alcohol and then in cellosolve.

Transfer to a drop of clove oil on a slide until clear.

Wash out the clove oil with xylene. Any residiual cloudiness will indicate that the water was not completely removed at the dehydration stage.

Put a drop of Canada Balsam in xylene on a clean slide and transfer the antenna to it. Arrange its position with needles.

Warm the slide a little.

Warm a cover slip and with forceps lower this until one edge meets the pool of Balsam.

Apply a wire clip to hold the cover slip down. Gentle pressure is all that is needed and a suitable clip can be made from a twisted paper clip.

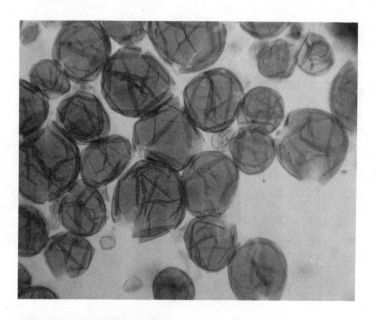

Fig. 30   Chalk brood – empty spore cases.

Put the slide away in a warm place to dry and harden.

Finally, when the Balsam is quite hard, clear away any excess with a knife and clean the slide with xylene.

After a little practice it will become easy to estimate just the right amount of Balsam to use so that it will completely fill the space between cover slip and slide and no more.

It is not necessary to ring Balsam mounts.

CHALK BROOD (Pericystis Apis)

The chalky covering to dead larvea consists of a tangled mass of mycelium and is of little interest to the microscopist. The characteristic black fruiting bodies are worth looking at. They are formed after the union of two hyphae. The round black or dark brown balls can be up to 400 microns in diameter and each contains spore balls about 30 microns across and, in turn, each of these hold hundreds of spores about 3 x 2 microns.

It is difficult to make a good permanent mount of the fruiting bodies. Try glycerine jelly with no pressure on the cover slip or lacto phenol.

CHITIN

All chitinous parts will need bleaching and macerating except wings and the sting apparatus.

CORNEA OF A COMPOUND EYE

With a scalpel slice off a good portion of a compound eye.

Invert in a watch glass in a few drops of 50% alcohol and clear away all the soft internal parts. The cornea is an extension of the exoskeleton and is hard. The easiest way to do this is to hold the edge of the cornea with the fine forceps, concave side up, and patiently remove all the adhering parts of the ommatidia with scalpel, needle and small camel hair brush.

Make three short cuts round the perimeter of the cornea with the scissors. This will allow the cornea to lay flatter, although it will be impossible to get it quite flat.

Cut a microslide tranversely into strips 1 in. by about $\frac{3}{8}$ in.

Place the cleaned cornea in the centre of one of these slips with slips of good quality notepaper on either side.

Add a second slip of glass and bind the two together tightly with cotton.

Immerse in alcohol for 24 hours then pour off the alcohol and replace with cellosolve. Leave for half-an-hour.

Punch out three small wads from thin card – visiting card or a little thinner. A No. 2 hollow punch will give you wads $\frac{3}{32}$ in. in diameter. In the absence of a punch, cut tiny squares of card.

Touch one side of each wad with Canada Balsam and space them, sticky side down, on a microslide equidistant round what will be the edge of the cover slip you propose to use. (Use four wads if you are using square cover slips – one at each corner.) This can be done previously to allow the Balsam on the wads to dry.

Remove the piece of cornea from between the glass slips and arrange it centrally between the wads and add a touch of Canada Balsam to each wad.

Add a further touch of Balsam at two places on the very edge of the cornea to anchor it. Be careful not to let this run under the cornea.

Carefully lower a cover slip and allow to dry.

If the cornea were mounted in Balsam or glycerine jelly it would become practically invisible because the refractive index of the cornea is so nearly that of the mountant.

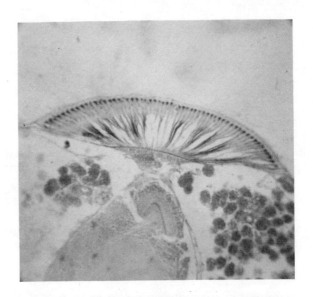

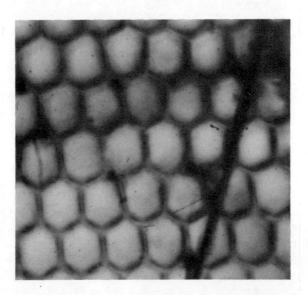

Fig. 31 Compound eye. Top, section through compound eye of worker showing ommatidia leading down to basement membrane (sometimes rather loosely called the 'retina'). Bottom, hexagonal facets of cornea.

The lens-like nature of the facets of the cornea can be demonstrated as follows:

Place the slide on the microscope under the X40 objective and focus.

Rack the microscope up until the image is just out of focus and at the same time rack the substage condenser down a little.

In front of the lamp place an opaque card in which you have cut a simple design – a cross or a 'V' will do. The cut out design need be no bigger than $\frac{1}{16}$ in to $\frac{1}{8}$ in.

By manipulating the microscope focus and the substage condenser at the same time you will be able to focus the aerial image of the design multiplied – one image for each facet.

EUROPEAN FOUL BROOD (Streptococcus Pluton)

Make smears with negative stain exactly as described for American Foul Brood, taking similar precautions as to cleanliness and sterilisation.

The cocci are about 1.3 x 1 micron – sometimes slightly less. As the name implies they are pointed at the ends. They often congregate in chains, end-to-end, or 'rosettes' – a clump of cocci apparently adhering at the pointed ends.

Whereas in American Foul Brood an almost pure culture of the bacteria occurs, in the case of European Foul Brood, especially in the advanced stages of decomposition, rods of Bacterium Euridice and Bacterium Alvei are often numerous. Neither of these resemble the causative organisms of American Foul Brood.

Although it is not a microscopic technique it may be of interest to note here details of the 'Milk Test'. This will distinguish between the two bacterial brood diseases most frequently met.

Place a drop of fresh milk (not the UHT kind) on a slide and rub into it a piece of scale or other diseased material. Scales are best. Rub up with a matchstick for ten seconds, no more. A firm curd will form, in AFB in about 30 seconds to a maximum of somewhat less than a minute. In EFB the time to form a curd is never less than 80 seconds and is usually more like two minutes.

It is, of course, necessary to time the test accurately and carefully, noting the exact time the scale goes into the milk. Use a stopwatch if one is available.

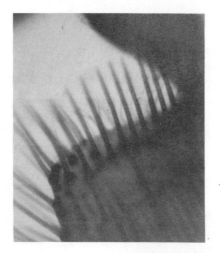
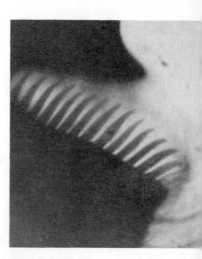
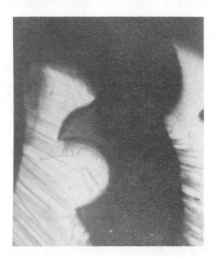

Fig. 32 Three reasons for caution in bleaching. Rastellum and pollen comb from third leg and antenna cleaner from first leg. In each case, if bleaching is allowed to proceed too far the stiff hairs and spines become difficult to see when devoid of colour.

EXOSKELETON

Sternites, tergites, spiracles, legs and feet cut off to include part of the tarsus all make good permanent mounts.

 Bleach, macerate, clear and mount as described for the antennae.

GLANDS

Pharyngeal glands. With the scissors cut off just above the mandibles. Best results are obtained with nurse bees. Insert the tips of the fine forceps and draw out the gland from one side. Repeat for the other side.

Alternatively, the pharyngeal glands can be dissected out as noted in the section dealing with the dissection of the head.

Post cerebral, thoracic salivary and abdominal glands all need to be dissected out.

There is a simple way of fixing, staining and making a permanent mount of the glands in one operation.

Place a drop of lacto-phenol to which you have added a little aniline blue on a slide. Lower the gland into this and add a cover slip. Try to use only sufficient lacto-phenol to fill the cover slip and no more.

Ring with nail varnish – two coats at least.

A stock solution of aniline blue in lacto-phenol is a useful thing to keep.

NOSEMA (Nosema Apis)

Spores are cylindrical with rounded ends about 4 x 2 microns. They are often described in the books as being like 'rice grains' – a singularly poor description.

The spores are hyaline and have a much higher refractive index than water so that in a routine watery smear they stand out well with hard black outlines.

Spores are likely to be much more numerous than in cases of Amoeba infection and, as a result of the lifecycle of the pathogen are to be found within the lumen of the ventriculus.

The 'mass' technique as described under 'Amoeba' is particularly suitable and quick for routine examinations. Permanent slides may be made with negative stain as smears or, unstained, in glycerine jelly.

MITOSIS

This most interesting chromosome multiplication stage of cell growth is of such universal biological significance that a slide or two of different stages should be in every microscopist's collection.

I have to confess that I have never succeeded in producing a really satisfactory example from bees but have had to rely on botanical material. The process is the same although the number of chromosomes is different of course.

The most fruitful sources (and the most easily handled) are the growing tips of onion or bean (vicia faba) roots.

Follow the schedule given under 'Sectioning'. An alternative stain worth trying is chlorazol black. Instead of stages 19, 20 and 21 in the schedule, immerse in an alcoholic solution of chlorazol black for two minutes, rinse in 50% alcohol, then differentiate in dilute Milton. After this follow the schedule from stage 22 onwards.

POLLEN

The beekeeping microscopist will want to build up his own collection of type slides of pollens so as to make a reference libruary of known pollens. Apart from general interest and the intrinsic beauty of the pollen grains, such a collection is of inestimable value in identifying pollens found in honey (even one's own honey gives surprises sometimes!).

The only reliable way is to make slides with pollen taken from the freshly opened anthers of flowers.

1. Bring your chosen flowers indoors and stand them in a glass of water in a warm room for a few hours.
2. Shake a dusting of pollen from the anthers on to a clean microslide.
3. Add two drops of di-ethyl ether or acetone. This will spread the grains and dissolve off the waxy/oily material present in most pollens.
4. Repeat 3.
5. Dry on the hot plate for two minutes.
6. Add a drop of stained glycerine jelly.
7. Cover with cover slip.
8. Return to hot plate for five minutes.
9. Place the slide in a cool place for 24 hours.
10. Label.
11. Ring with nail varnish.

N.B. Stained Glycerine jelly:

Make up glycerine jelly as shown under 'Formulae and Hints'. While still molten add *drop by drop* an aqueous solution of basic fuchsin. It is very easy to overdo this and tastes vary as to the depth of colour wanted. I like to keep two bottles of stained jelly, one only just tinted and the other deeper – a bit less deep than a good claret. In making my slides I use a drop of each jelly placed roughly just inside where the cover slip will be but on opposite sides. The two jellies coalesce and give me a gradation of stain.

Extraction of pollen from honey by methods available to the amateur

1. Sedimentation

Given sufficient time particles in suspension in any liquid will settle to the bottom of the container. Honey, especially good honey, is very viscous so the process may take a very long time.

Method:

(a) Take 10 g. sample of honey and dilute it with at least ten times the volume of warm water.

(b) Stir until completely dissolved. If any crystallisation is present heat and stir until all crystals are dissolved.

(c) Pour into a fairly wide container and allow to settle. A 1 lb. honey jar will do. Coarser particles and large pollen grains will settle in about two hours, but it is preferable to leave overnight.

(d) After 24 hours carefully decant all the water except the last $\frac{1}{4}$ in.

(e) Add more water, stir well and leave for another 24 hours.

(f) Repeat (e), gradually reducing the amount of water and the size of the container until finishing with a small tapered tube. Small (4 in.) test tubes are satisfactory.

(g) Decant *carefully* the water from the test tube.

(h) The sediment which will be visible can now be sucked up with a fine pipette.

The *disadvantages* of sedimentation are:

1. It is slow and time consuming.
2. There is always some doubt as to whether all the pollen has been collected.

The *advantages* are:

1. It is cheap and simple. No special apparatus is needed.
2. Differential collection of pollens of different weights can be carried out.

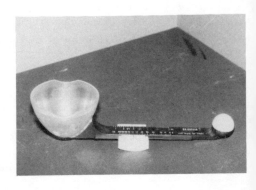

Fig. 33 Two 'balances'. Left, for balancing centrifuge tubes. This is made from an old apothecariees' pocket scale with the pans removed and replaced by strands of picture wire twisted into circles to hold the tubes. Right, weighing balance marked in grams and ounces. It is surprisingly accurate. Obtainable from wine-making stores.

2. Centrifuging

Method:

(a) Take a 10 g. sample of honey into a 50 ml. beaker.
(b) Add warm water to make 25 to 30 ml.
(c) Warm and stir. See that all crystals are dissolved.
(d) Pour into 15 ml. centrifuge tubes.
(e) Balance tubes.
(f) Centrifuge – about 7 to 10 minutes.
(g) Decant and transfer sediment to one tube with water.
(h) Balance tubes with water.
(i) Re-centrifuge. Five minutes.
(j) Decant tube with sediment.
(k) Sediment can now be sucked up with a fine pipette.

The *disadvantages* of this method are:

1. A centrifuge is needed (but this can be improvised).
2. Some method of balancing the tubes is needed.

The *advantages* are:

1. It is quick.
2. It is accurate and can be standardised. All solid particles can be collected even if longer centrifuging is needed.

Mounting:

1. Transfer sediment to the centre of a 3 in. x 1 in. microslide.
2. Spread sediment with tip of pipette to a patch about 19 mm in diameter.
3. Dry on warm plate (about 10 minutes).
4. Add drop of melted, stained, jelly.
5. Add cover glass.
6. Place on warm plate (about 10 to 15 minutes).
7. Allow to cool.
8. When quite cold, clean off any surplus jelly carefully with small camel hair brush.
9. Dry, and when quite dry ring with varnish to make a permanent mount (nail varnish (any colour) is satisfactory).

PRESERVATION OF DISSECTIONS

Sometimes there is a need to preserve dissections for future reference. A good preservative is 50% glycerine. The dissections can go straight into this form from the 50% alcohol used in the dissecting pan.

Instead of embedding your bee in the wax pan before starting, make shallow trays about 25 mm x 12 mm and 1 mm to 5 mm deep out of sheet zinc or copper. Fill these trays with molten wax and embed your bees in them.

Alternatively, cut pieces of stiff plastic 25 mm x 12 mm and cover one side with a molten mix of wax and about 10% resin. This makes a stronger mix with more 'hold' than pure wax. Embed the bees in the wax/resin layer and attach the plastic slip to the wax surface of the dissecting dish by melting the wax by each corner of the slip with a warm wire.

Having finished your dissections they can be kept for a long time in small ceramic (or similar) pots in 50% glycerine. The metal trays will sink; the plastic slips will float. See that they float face down.

An elegant way to preserve dissections, but involving a little more trouble, is to house them in 'micro jars' made of perspex. Make (cut with a coping saw) a 'U' piece with a cavity of 27 mm x 20 mm x 7 mm deep with plain pieces on each side, the three pieces cemented together with epoxy resin glue. This will make a more sure bond if the surfaces which will meet are roughed up on fine emery paper. Cut a 'lid' to fit the top and secure it to the jar by

Fig. 34 Top, small trays made of sheet zinc and filled with wax to hold specimens for dissection and subsequent preservation. Bottom, perspex 'micro-jars' for completed dissections (double needle shown in top illustration).

two countersunk 6 BA screws. Do not attach the lid permanently. A smear of vaseline will be adequate before screwing down and will enable you to remove air bubbles and top up with more glycerine.

We are indebted to the late H. A. Dade for the idea of these 'micro jars.'

PROBOSCIS

Remove the head of a freshly killed bee.

Pin it 'face' down on the wax in a dissecting pan with a double needle.

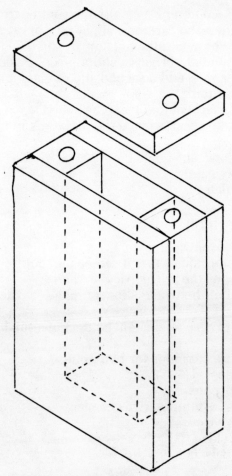

Fig. 35 Details of construction of perspex micro-jar. These consist of a 'U' piece of $\frac{1}{4}$ in. thick perspex (or two $\frac{1}{8}$ in. pieces cemented together) sandwiched between two pieces of $\frac{1}{8}$ in. clear perspex. The internal dimensions of the 'cavity' are not critical, but should be not less than $\frac{7}{8}$ in. by $\frac{1}{2}$ in. They could be a little larger than this with advantage.

The lid is held on by two screws driven into the solid upright arms of the 'U' piece. They can be either No. 6 countersunk screws, in which case the holes need to be tapped or, alternatively, round-headed self-tapping screws.

Flood with 50% alcohol.

The proboscis is likely to be in the folded position. If this is the case extend the parts with a needle.

Detach the cardines from the point of their articulation in the fossa with a scalpel. The whole proboscis should now come away free from the head.

A sheet of membrane (actually the continuation of the mouth cavity) lies across the cardines, stipes and prementum. Tear this with a needle. The apparatus can now be spread out flat.

Arrange on a slip of glass, add a piece of good quality note-paper on either side, add a second slip of glass and tie the whole together with cotton.

Immerse in alcohol for at least 24 hours.

Cut the cotton and remove the proboscis to cellosolve for 15 minutes.

Clear in clove oil.

Wash in xylene.

Mount in Balsam.

PROVENTRICULUS

Dissect out a proventriculus.

Slit it up one side so that it can be laid out flat, but be careful to avoid damaging the proventricular valve.

Lay out flat between slips of glass as described under 'Proboscis.'

Immerse in alcohol for an hour or overnight if more convenient.

Stain in borax carmine for 15 minutes.

Wash in alcohol (50%).

Wash in alcohol.

Cellosolve 10 minutes (two changes).

Clear in clove oil.

Wash in xylene.

Mount in Balsam.

SPERMATOZOA

Use a mature drone or the spermatheca from a discarded (but mated) queen. Get some of the spermatozoa into a watch glass with a little warm water and hold in the palm of the hand to keep warm for a few minutes. When taken from seminal vesicle or spermatheca the tails are doubled and thrown into three coils. The object of keeping them warm is to allow them to become active. When they do so they uncoil and the tails begin to lash.

The tails are quite long – about $\frac{1}{4}$ mm but are only 0.5 microns wide. The head is about 10 microns long and is the part carrying the genetic material.

The axial strand of the tail and about half the head will take up stain.

With a glass rod place a drop of the suspension on a grease-free slide and spread it about to a little more than the area of the cover slip you propose to use.

Allow to dry without heat.

When quite dry add a drop of your chosen stain and warm the slide gently.

Leave for half-an-hour, but do not allow the stain to dry up. Add more stain if necessary.

Wash under gently running water.

With a pipette, add a few drops of alcohol and *immediately* wash this off with water.

Allow to dry.

When quite dry, add a drop of Balsam and a cover slip.

STING

Dissect out the sting. With little difficulty the whole apparatus, including muscles, poison sac, nerve ganglion and proctiger, etc. will come away in one piece.

Make slides in glycerine jelly to show dorsal and side aspects. This will make a rather thick mount so wads to support the cover slip, as mentioned when we dealt with the cornea, will be a help. Do not use too much pressure. You need a mount which will show the apparatus undistorted.

To display the plates, place a dissected out sting in 10% caustic potash and allow to macerate for two days.

Remove from the potash to water in a watch glass, and with needles and brush, remove any remaining pieces of muscle, etc.

Remove the proctiger. This is attached to the oblong plates by a sheet of membrane. Its removal will allow the sting shaft and plates to be flattened out.

Place between two slips of glass, tie with cotton and immerse in alcohol for 24 hours.

Remove from alcohol and rinse in fresh alcohol.

Clear in clove oil.

Wash out clove oil with xylene.

Mount in Canada Balsam and set aside to harden with a clip to hold the cover slip down – not heavy pressure.

TRACHEAE

Treat as noted under 'Acarine', but a light staining with borax-carmine will bring out the detail more clearly. If stain is used, dehydrate and clear before mounting in Balsam.

WINGS

Wings need no treatment other than a soak in cellosolve for half-an-hour, followed by a wash in xylene.

Mount in Balsam in pairs with a clip to give gentle pressure.

Try to arrange the pairs so that the hamuli of the rear wings are adjacent to the folds in the front wings which they engage.

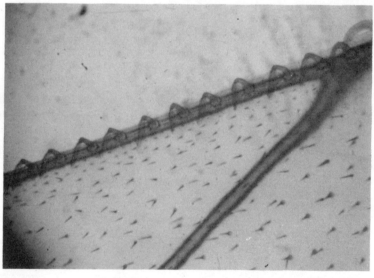

Fig. 36 Hamuli (hooks) on leading edge of hind wing. These engage in a fold on the trailing edge of the fore wing.

FURTHER READING

Many of the following titles are now out of print. This is a pity because some of them have never been surpassed. They come on the second-hand market from time to time.

Abercrombie M, Hickman C J & Johnson M L
   A Dictionary of Biology (Penguin)

Bailey L
   Honeybee Pathology (Academic Press)

Carpenter W B
   The Microscope (Churchill)

Dade H A
   The Anatomy and Dissection of the Honeybee (IBRA)

Dade H A
   The Laboratory Diagnosis of Honeybee Diseases (Queckett Microscopical Club)

Hodges D
   Pollen Loads of the Honeybee (IBRA)

Howes F N
   Plants and Beekeeping (Faber)

Lee A B
   The Microtomist's Vade-Mecum (Churchill)

Moore P D & Webb J A
   An Illustrated Guide to Pollen Analysis (Hodder & Stoughton)

Olliver C W
   The Intelligent Use of the Microscope (Chapman & Hall)

Pringle J W S
   Insect Flight (Cambridge University Press)

Peacock H A
   Elementary Microtechnique (Arnold)

Sawyer R

    Pollen Identification for Beekeepers (University College
    . Cardiff Press)

Snodgrass R E

    Anatomy and Physiology of the Honeybeee (McGraw Hill)
    N.B. Later editions were published by Constable under
        the title 'The Anatomy of the Honeybee'

Wigglesworth V B

    The Principles of Insect Morphology (Methuen)

Wood J G

    Common Ojects of the Microscope (Routledge)

INDEX

GLOSSARY

The following is a list of some of the anatomical and optical terms used in this book and in others dealing with insect morphology. Plural forms are noted where they differ from the Anglicised addition of 's' and the meanings of root words are given when this might be helpful.

Some terms are used in the specific context of microscopy. For instance 'objective' in normal speech means 'aim' or 'desired end'. Here it means the lens attached to the lower end of a microscope tube.

The list is not, and does not pretend to be exhaustive.

Abbe condenser. A simple system of lenses below the stage of a microscope. Its function is to receive light reflected from the plane mirror and focus it in the plane of the specimen.

Acinus (pl. **acini**), (a berry). The cellular nodules on the duct of a gland producing the glandular secretion.

Anterior. The fore part.

Autolysis. The self-dissolution, i.e. decomposition, of tissue after the death of their cells due to the action of their own enzymes.

Basalare (basis, base and ala, a wing). A small plate near the base of the roots of a bee's wings. Muscles control pitch and angle of attack in flight.

Carapace. The hard exoskeleton of an insect. Not usually used in the case of bees, more often applied to beetles etc.

Cardo (pl. **cardines**) a hinge. The chitinised processes on which the proboscis of the bee swings below the mouth.

Chemotaxis. Movement of an organism or cell (e.g. a gamete) in response to a chemical stimulus. It is thought that such a process assists spermatozoa to travel into the spermatheca of a queen after mating.

Chitin (chiton, a tunic). The hard nitrogenous material forming the covering layer of the cuticle of insects. Also used in the formation of strengthening struts inside the body and elsewhere. It is a polysaccharide with long fibrous molecules.

Chromosomes. Thread shaped bodies which occur in the nuclei of all plant and animal cells. They exist in pairs and only become visible at the times of division (meiosis and meiosis) when the threads coil into a comparatively thick spiral.

Clypeus (a shield). The front facing part of the head of the honeybee. It forms the greater part of the 'face'.

Cytoplasm. The protoplasmic contents of a cell except the nucleus.

Cytology. The study of cells.

Diaphragm. Sheet of tissue, part muscle and part membrane. In the honeybee there are two, one ventral and one dorsal. Wave like movements of the diaphragm assist the dissemination of the blood.

Dorsal and **Ventral** (dorsum, the back and venter, the belly). The back or underside of the insect.

Epithelium (epi and thele, a nipple). Meaning extended to a thin layer of tissue.

Flagellum (a little whip). The segmented part of the antenna.

Foramen (pl. **foramina**). The hole in the back of the head through which connecti[...] organs pass into the thorax.

Fossa (ditch or trench). The U shaped hollow at the back of the head in which the p[...] boscis is articulated.

Frons (pl. **frontes**). The brow or forehead.

Furca (pl. **furcae**) (a fork). Strong bridge-shaped chitinous processes arching across t[...] thorax internally, adding strength and protecting the ganglia.

Ganglion (a tumour or swelling). A small solid mass of nervous tissue along the cent[...] nervous system. They are connected by double nerve cords, the commissure.

Gena (pl. **genae**) (a cheek). The side pieces of the head.

Hamulus (pl. **hamuli**) (a small hook). A row of hooks on the leading edges of the hi[...] wings. In flight they engage with folds at the trailing edges of the fore wings.

Hypopharyngeal glands. Glands lying above the pharynx and below the frons. Th[...] consist of a long coiled tubule to which are connected by short side tubules many sm[...] round bodies, the acini. These produce the brood food. The glands are plump in you[...] and over wintered bees but shrink after nursing.

Histology. The study of tissues.

Hyaline (hualos – glass). Clear, transparent.

Hypha (pl. **hyphae**). A thin filament.

Labium. The lower lip.

Labrum. The upper lip.

Lumen (literally light). The cavity or space within a tube.

Maceration. Softening by soaking. The process is accelerated by immersion in a we[...] solution of caustic potash.

Malpighian tubules. Fine tubes, the walls of which consist of a single layer of cells. Th[...] absorb notrogenous waste from the blood. Analogous to the vertibrate kidney. They j[...] the digestive tract where the small gut joins the ventriculus.

Meiosis. The so called 'reduction division' of cells. At the end of the process, daugh[...] cells contain half the original number of chromosomes, i.e. they are haploid.

Mitosis. The normal growth division of cells. All parts divide so that daughter cells [...] exact reproductions of the parent cell. They contain a full complement of chromoson[...] (are diploid).

Nuclei. In the fields of microscopy and histology/cytology this word means the nucle[...] biological cells, **not** the meaning applied by beekeepers to small five frame colonie[...] bees.

Objective. Here again is a word used in a specialised sense. The objective of a mic[...] scope is that system of lenses screwed into the lower end of the tube, i.e. nearest [...] object on the stage.

Occiput. The back of the head.

Oesophagus. That part of the gut between pharynx and stomach. Its function is me[...] to pass food along its length. Usually by peristalsis.

Ommatidia. The separate elements of the compound eye. Each has its own sim[...] refractive system and light sensitive cell. Each is surrounded by opaque pigment.

Paraglossa. (pl. **paraglossae**). The structures at the side of the glossa (tongue).

Pharynx. The throat.

Phragma (pl. **phragmae**) (a fence). Rigid fence-like extensions on the inside of the e[...] skeleton which serve as strengthening members and as attachment points for muscles.

108

octiger (proktos, the anus and gero, to bear). The terminal abdominal segment which cries the anus. In the bee it is firmly attached to the oblong plates of the sting echanism.

opodeum (pro, in front of and pous, a stalk). The fourth segment of the thorax. ructurally it is really part of the abdomen. It carries the largest spiracle in the bee but, her curiously, it is not the spiracle invaded by the acarine mite.

mus. The curved extension of the sting lancet. It is articulated to the triangular plate the sting apparatus..

stellum (little rake). The row of teeth attached to the inside lower edge of the tibia. It used to scrape pollen off the hairs of the basitarsus.

ape (scapus, an upright stem or shaft). The rigid rod-like part of the antenna nearest head.

ta. A bristle.

ermatheca (sperma and theka, a container). A sperical receptacle in the abdomen of queen in which sperm is stored after successful mating.

ernites. The ventral plates of the exoskeleton.

balare. A small plate below, and to the rear of, the forewing. Attached muscles con-l flight (see also basalare).

ture. A seam.

ntorium (pl. **tentoria**). Like a tent pole. The internal chitinised pillars strengthening the x structure of the head.

rgite. The 'back' plates of the exoskeleton.

ntriculus. The stomach or mid gut of insects.

rtex. The crown of the head.